Dearest C...
Words can not express
how I feel about you & your
family!! :)

THE THINGS I'VE SEEN PEOPLE
DO WITH AND
WITHOUT FOOD

Happy that you
picked this up &
grateful for you!! :)

Yours in health &
wellbeing,

Deb :)

The Things I've Seen People Do With and Without Food

First Edition.
Paperback ISBN: 978-0-578-98180-2

Library of Congress Control Number: 2021918245

Cover design by Gary MacKnight
All rights owned by Debra Spector
Edited Adele Brinkley

10 9 8 7 6 5 4 3 2 1

THE THINGS I'VE SEEN PEOPLE DO WITH AND WITHOUT FOOD

DEBRA SPECTOR MS, RDN, CDN

*This book is dedicated
to those of you who have openly shared your essays
and understand how misunderstood the struggle
with eating disorders is.*

*I am also dedicating
this book to those of you brave enough
to begin or continue on your path towards recovery.*

I know, your struggle is real.

Table of Contents

PROLOGUE

I have been a Registered Dietitian/Nutritionist (RDN) in private practice since 1990 where I specialize in eating disorders and felt compelled to put together this book of relational essays. When I decided to write about eating disorders, I took a different approach. Instead of scientific data and test cases, I gathered my patient's stories together to paint a vivid and relatable picture. In addition, I have included 23 pieces from recovered patients, parents of recovered patients, and professionals I've had the pleasure of knowing, with their permission.

This past year, and living through a pandemic, has ultimately changed our lives forever. It has caused increased levels of stress, anxiety, depression, and isolation. Add to that a great reliance on a virtual world filled with misinformation and societal pressure, food safety issues and insecurity, an influx of body identification and you have the perfect storm for a mental health crisis and an explosion of people who are struggling to gain control of something and as a result, a surge in eating disorders.

People struggle every day. Unfortunately, most people with eating disorders struggle internally and feel misunderstood. People in their lives can not relate to the inner dialogue and beliefs they have, so they struggle alone. My patients are so frustrated with the messages society and the media have insinuated that we need to be robotic or less than human. In this one size doesn't fit the same world we live in, I have found a way to provide stories that are truly relational so each person can feel special in their skin.

My intent on putting this book of relational essays together is to help those of you who struggle WITH or WITHOUT food to know that you are not alone in the world. Most people just keep their eating problems hidden. They do not express themselves because they feel people will think they are crazy or because other people just do not "get it."

An estimated 30 million Americans will be diagnosed with an eating disorder at some point in their lives. Simply put, an eating disorder is an addiction. Food addiction. Not so easy to stop or, as I say, "turn off."

On the outside, someone may appear too thin or overweight, but on the inside, a lot more is going on. The amount of "chatter," which is a person's inner thoughts associated with food, weight, and body image, is exhausting. How much mental space or emotional energy do your eating habits take up? Do you notice your self-worth changing based on the food choices you have made that day, the day before, or on where you are going to be eating tomorrow?

Let's be honest, you do not just wake up one day and decide, "I am going to stop eating today." No, the changes you make with food, weight, and body image usually show up for a reason. Like many forms of addiction, it's about control or the beginning of a "bad behavior" as a coping skill that you've begun to do repeatedly until it actually becomes a "bad habit" that, like any habit, is difficult to break.

For this book of essays, to be diagnosed as having an eating disorder, you likely meet the Diagnostic and Statistical Manual of Mental Disorders (DSM IV or DSM V) criteria. The term "disordered eating" is quite different from an actual eating disorder. Disordered eating is a label for people who engage in behaviors around food that are disordered but may not have been evaluated for or are not severe enough to have reached a formal diagnosis. I believe that in America dieting is a form of disordered eating.

The truth is, lack of consistent criteria used to diagnose and determine a person with an eating disorder plus shame and stigma and lack of medical practitioner insight often leave sufferers feeling unheard or not good enough at "being sick" to get the proper diagnosis or help they need. Over the years, I cannot even begin to count how many patients I have seen who present with active behaviors, such as starving themselves, not drinking any fluids, or throwing up their food. But, because they are not emaciated, their insurance companies will not provide them the proper care and allow them to enter into an inpatient setting. The unfortunate truth is that many people who suffer do not receive the proper care they need because of their medical coverage and continue to suffer.

Sadly, many health care providers claim to have had experience treating eating disorders but do not, or some who have no experience with them at all and overlook them, leaving some individuals with thoughts that they are okay and do not have a problem.

To be clear, I do not do this work alone. Yes, I have upheld my private practice since 1990 and work in an outpatient setting, but I am not alone. As a pediatrician with whom I have shared many patients once said, "Anyone who thinks they can do this work alone, actually knows nothing." An outpatient team usually consists of a RDN, a therapist with the right form of training and area of expertise in the patients' struggles, an MD who understands that an eating disorder is not just a number on the scale but can provide empathy and guidance, and often a psychiatrist who specializes in eating disorders. This team must work collaboratively for the patients to get the necessary care they need.

For my anorexic patients, the most common thing they hear is "What's your problem? Just eat." As if the cure is really that easy. I do not think it is. For those of them who, unfortunately, did not get the right guidance, they honestly think that just the act of eating is all they need to do. Or following a meal plan and measuring and/ or weighing food is what they do when they are recovered. Well, sorry, that is not the answer.

So much more is needed to help them to understand how much they need to eat. To feel "okay" with letting themselves eat. To learn and understand the feeling of hunger and to "give in" not push the food away as a measure of success and self-care and not a sign of failure. To give themselves permission to "feel full" and not be afraid of that feeling. I am not talking about stuffed, uncomfortable full. Regular, normal full, which most of my patients have never felt.

Change is extremely hard! Most people would rather stay stuck in their circumstances then make a change. Although they may be aware of their problems or addictions, let's be perfectly honest. To have someone who specializes in their form of addiction point out their shortcomings, have them feel accountable, and guide them on an exceedingly difficult journey is not easy to accept.

4

Quite honestly, what is the alternative? Are you happy? Genuinely happy? Are you enjoying being in the moment? Enjoying the people and the things you love? I highly doubt that you are. That inner voice (or as I call it, the "uninvited guest") will not allow it to happen. The voice owns you and wants you to waste every waking moment consumed with the desire and/or cravings you have for food.

I wish I had a magic wand or fairy dust that I could use for some of my patients and "make" the chatter go away. I wish I could tell the world that it is not just about weight and the number on a scale. I wish I could educate every health care professional so they would be able to empathize with these people who struggle every waking moment and guide them in the right direction. Obviously, I cannot. I am one person in this huge world. My sincere hope in putting together this book of relational essays is to help provide hope and to show people who suffer with overwhelming thoughts about food, weight, and body image that they are not alone.

Sometimes our days bring difficult, but meaningful, choices. Ask yourself: do I travel on this road and feel anxious, or do I travel the road I've been asked to travel that is the clearer, better choice although I may have thoughts of uncertainty, fear, and even discomfort? If you choose the road you're being asked to travel on, you may hit potholes, a tiny bit of traffic, maybe even get into a fender bender, but I promise you, this road is the better choice because your destination is recovery and there is no discomfort in that.

For many years, I have wanted to put this book together to let people know that there is at least one person (Me) who totally gets what they are going through. I want to share some of my many

5

recovered patients' achievements and stories of their individual journeys, some of which I am certain you can relate to. I want you to hear those recovered patients' parents' fears and thoughts, plus many of my colleagues' opinions about what they have seen in their offices and in their own experiences.

The most important reason I have finally written this book is to provide hope if you decide to embark on one of the most difficult journeys of your life... Believe me... RECOVERY WILL BE WORTH IT!

Your Struggle Is Real

Deb-ism #1

Addiction recovery is challenging work.
You have the choice to surround
yourself with a positive environment or
not. After all, a recovered alcoholic does
not "choose" to read their newspaper in
a bar do they?

MY STRUGGLE WAS REAL

Today is the day, full disclosure. It took me three years to get enough courage to "come clean" because I was worried how people would react once I did. Then, I decided there are a lot of people just like me out there who don't understand why they're suffering and perhaps this confession will help.

Since 1990, I have specialized and held a private practice in which I have guided people of all ages, genders, ethnic backgrounds, shapes and sizes on a very difficult and often misunderstood journey towards recovery of an eating disorder. Over the years, many of them have asked if I personally have ever had an eating disorder. No, I say, but I grew up with people close to me who have suffered and many who still suffer, so I get it. All of it.

An eating disorder is an addiction and addiction can manifest in many different ways. That's where I personally can relate. Just like many of you, life has thrown me a lot of curve balls. Some actually hit me with a force and speed that literally knocked me to the ground and took all the breath out of my lungs. I've cried, sometimes for days, to the point where my eyelids were so swollen that I could barely see out of my eyes. I have prayed. I have looked up to the sky and asked G-d, my higher power, my grandma and my grandpa to show me the way. Help me. Guide me. Stop this pain.

It took me a lifetime to realize the only person I had to ask for help from was me. Yes, I still struggle. Yes, I still pray. Yes, I still look up to the sky and ask for guidance. I have learned and memorized the serenity prayer, but only this year have I really learned and understood the meaning of the actual words.

"G-d grant me serenity to accept the things I cannot change (others, the environment, how other people react, what they say and do), the courage to change the things I can (me, how I react, the ability to say how I feel and to say no, and set healthy boundaries without feeling guilty), and the wisdom to know the difference."

The wisdom to know the difference, to me, is where the power is. In my mind, the true definition behind the serenity prayer has helped in my recovery from a very misunderstood form of addiction called "codependency."

I remember almost to the day, when one of my oldest, dearest friends told me I had this problem. Confused, I looked at her and said, "What are you talking about? You've known me for what feels like forever and know that I'm independent and can do anything on my own." She said, "Deb, I know that, but that's not what codependency is."

So, just like anything I don't understand or have knowledge about, I began my research. Codependency is an emotional internal addiction. It usually shows up at a young age and is actually organic in that it just evolves. The real place codependency shows up in is intimate relationships, which as a single woman was my biggest challenge. I was a textbook example. Going above and beyond for the people I loved the most, despite deep down not having enough strength or energy left for me. Fearing their reaction if I said no to their needs or demands. Not being able to say no to something or someone asking me to do something, because I was afraid if I did, I would lose them, or they would be mad at me. Losing myself because I was too busy taking care of others.

The world needs giving, loving, compassionate and empathic people. However, you also deserve reciprocity. Know you're supposed to receive love, kindness, and compassion in return for giving them. The hardest test of recovery was learning to set boundaries with my family, closest friends, ex-husband, and ex-fiancé. I loved these people more than myself and would and did anything for them without hesitation. Isn't that what people who love are supposed to do?

Then it hit me... I was exhausted. Depleted. I needed help, so I entered therapy. This wonderful woman who specialized in codependency (recommended by my friend who pointed out to me that I had this problem) helped gently guide me on a heart wrenching, costly journey. As I tested the waters and found my voice with the people I loved the most, a huge shift occurred. They didn't understand what was going on.

I remember going over to my brother and sister-in-law's house and openly sharing with them a bit of this form of addiction that had such a tight grip on me, I was afraid to let go. They didn't understand and said almost the exact same thing I had said to my friend when she first mentioned codependency to me. My sister-in-law replied, "Wow, that makes sense. Now, I understand why you and your brother had a rough year last year and were fighting all the time."

Have I lost some people in my journey? Yes. When I learned to find my voice, they didn't like the new song that I was singing. No problem. I'm blessed to have true and tried people by my side who didn't quit when I found my voice. Later, when I was in recovery, I learned they weren't worth trying to talk to in the first place because I now know they weren't listening.

Since discovering I had this form of addiction, my work with my patients who struggle with eating disorders has become much more relational. Many of them struggle with codependency as well.

I remember my last session with my therapist. She asked me to sit back, for she was going to tell me something that was going to be difficult to hear. Great, I thought, like this journey wasn't difficult enough. She asked me if I was ready to take accountability for my becoming and struggling with codependency. I understood what that meant and began to cry. She was telling me that I was the one who allowed all of what had happened to me in the past to occur, so I accepted it.

In recovery, do I get triggered? Yes. Do I engage in inappropriate behaviors? No. I put together this book of relational essays for you from someone who not only has struggled and recovered from addiction, but also from someone who, after 31 years of experience, totally understands what your struggle has been. I want to share some of your stories so your voices can be heard.

My message: You've got this. Moving forward in my journey to recover from codependency is the hardest thing I've ever gone through in my life of hardships, but I know it's possible. Recovery is possible.

Your Struggle Is Real

Deb-ism #2

Thoughts Are Thoughts, They Don't Become Behaviors Unless You Use

DINNER PARTY AND PIE

Scenario: You're sitting at work and completing a document you've been working on for the last few months when your significant other calls you to let you know that The CFO (Chief Financial Officer) of his company has just entered his office to ask him if he would like the Marketing Director position opening up in the next few months. You are so over the top excited for him that you blurt out, "That's wonderful. Let's have him and his wife over for dinner."

Your significant other thinks that is a wonderful idea, and you both plan a date after reviewing your joint calendars. So, with the rest of your day laid out to finish your document, you decide to take 20 minutes before your lunch break to plan the menu.

You remember that the CFO's wife is vegetarian, so your menu includes an appetizer and main course that has been true and tried over the top. Yummy. Then, it dawns on you. Whenever you've had dinner parties in the past, people have asked you what they should bring, and you've told them dessert, knowing that most people when they are asked to bring dessert bring what they like. At the end of the evening, you could ask them to take it home with them. Although they may not want to, the likelihood is stronger that they will if they like the choice they've brought.

But, you really don't know this couple, have never been out with them, and with this new position up for grabs and your significant other on the top five list, there is no way you're going to have him ask them to bring anything, even if they actually ask what to bring.

So, you decide on pie for dessert. Safe. Not hard to make. And doesn't everyone eat pie? Plus, it is your significant other's favorite dessert; therefore, if there are leftovers, he will be delighted.

Success. You have completed your menu plus dessert (not your work document). Off you go to lunch and treat yourself to something special for your amazing feat.

The night arrives, and all goes well. Laughter, tasty food, and a potential new position for your significant other is in place until the CFO's wife helps you clear the dishes and upon setting dirty plates down in the kitchen sees the pie. "Wow, you truly went above and beyond tonight and are a fabulous cook. I hope you don't feel insulted if I do not have dessert. You see, I am on a special diet. I already overdid it at dinner and cannot have dessert. I'm sure you understand." And the beginning to a long night of chatter from the "uninvited guest" begins.

While clearing the dinner plates with her, your mind goes into millions of directions. Why did she say I should understand? Does she think I'm on a diet? Does she think I am fat? What diet did she say she was on? What size do you think she wears? Damn, what size was she before she started her diet? Does she belong to a gym? I bet she can afford a personal trainer. When my significant other gets this new position, I am going to be able to afford one too and will join her gym and use her personal trainer. We can even be workout and diet buddies. And this chatter goes on for the rest of the evening. You try to keep up with the conversation over dessert, but you cannot shut it up. It is exhausting.

Your significant other comments about you making his favorite dessert, the CFO cannot wait to try it, and his wife says she is too full from dinner and will have to pass.

You cut three slices, and while you are eating your "sliver," you do not taste even a bit of it. In fact, your anxiety level within you has gone up so high on your internal emotional time scale that you want to gag and quite honestly are having trouble swallowing.

When they leave, your significant other hugs you and thanks you for such a successful and wonderful evening and heads to the bedroom. He did not even notice you struggling through dessert.

While cleaning up dessert, the leftover pie sits. It has visually morphed itself into something else. Something irresistible. You reach over and pull a piece of the crust off and pop it into your mouth. Now you finally give yourself permission to taste it without anyone watching or judging you. Then, you grab a clean spoon and taste the inside of the pie and its sweetness. Wow, this really came out awesome! Standing at the kitchen counter, you continue to have spoon after spoon of pie until half of it is gone. Suddenly, you hear your significant other call to you. "Hey babe, when you come up, can you please bring me a bottle of water?"

When you snap out of the "spoon to mouth behavior", you look down and see the damage you just did in approximately 10 minutes and feel disgusting. Every negative word you can imagine gets directed toward you...loser, weak, fat, disgusting. You throw the pie into the garbage and put coffee grounds over the top of it so you will not be tempted to eat it out of the garbage pail.

When you go up to the bedroom and hand your significant other his water bottle, you tell him that the pie accidentally fell off the counter onto the floor and needed it to be thrown away. You knew how much he loved it. Sorry.

In bed that night, you will not let him touch you. No intimacy. No snuggling. You feel fat, tell him you're exhausted, and spend the sleepless night thinking about the pie and how much you hate yourself. Good dinner party gone bad.

Your Struggle Is Real

Deb-ism #3

I Swear My Fridge Said:
"What The Hell
Do You Want Now"

THE FRIDGE

We've all seen it. Most of us own one and pass by it at least three times a day without a thought. The rectangular object that stands against the wall in one of the most occupied rooms in the house. I am sure you have figured out that it is the refrigerator in your kitchen. For many, this most often unnoticed object supplies only the cream for your morning coffee, the bottle of water you grab before you hit the gym, or the ketchup you need to put on your hamburger that was grilled. For others, it is an open, grab the item, and close the door. No emotional attachment whatsoever.

Unfortunately, that is not the way it goes for many of the patients I see. In and of itself, the kitchen is a dangerous place to be, let alone hang out. Within those walls holds an electronic piece of equipment that for many is a huge trigger. One of my patients said he needs to envision it with a skull and crossbones on it in order to stay away.

Many state that each time they walk into the kitchen, they open and close the refrigerator. Open, look, see nothing enticing, close. Three hours later, the same behavior. What are they looking for? Has anyone in the house gone grocery shopping in the last three hours for there to actually be more food to look for?

Some of my patients spend most of their waking time outside their own houses to avoid temptation from the rectangular box. The control comes when they are not present with it. So, they pay their costly mortgage or rent, perhaps have the American dream, and avoid enjoying being present within its walls to circumvent being alone with the rectangular box that constantly seems to be calling their names.

If you have even a glitter of fear of being alone with the rectangular box, why are you hanging out in the kitchen? Is that a "safe place" to do your homework? Talk on the phone with your sister-in-law? Type the final report for your team at work on your laptop? Write out the invitations to your daughter's sweet 16 party while sitting at the kitchen table? I highly doubt it, for the rectangular box is alone with you.

Let us look at one scenario together:

While in the kitchen doing your homework, you get up to get an eraser because the pencil that was in your backpack did not have one. While getting it, you walk by the fridge and reach in to grab a bottle of water, and what appears out of the corner of your eye is the leftover pasta dish your mom made that was so over the top yummy. Without blinking an eye, you reach in and grab a finger full of it. That is right; you do not even stop to get a fork. While you are chewing, the flavors try to hit your tongue, and you decide to pinch your fingers together for another try and another, and another. There you are, standing at the refrigerator with the door open with a continuous hand to mouth motion. At this point you are not even tasting, let alone getting your homework done. Then, you jump. Your sister calls out from the other room to come over to her, and your heart drops as you slam the door of the fridge shut. It is over, or is it? The actual act of eating may be over, but after going into your sister's room to see what she wanted, you return back to the kitchen to finish your homework.

You sit down, go back to the last exercise to reread it since you lost your place, and there it sits. You see it out of the corner of your eye. The rectangular box. You have lost focus. All you can think about is that delicious pasta dish and how much you really want a little more. You try to regroup and get back to your homework, for it is getting late, and you still need to shower. It is at this exact point you hear it: the uninvited guest. You caused the chatter by going back and forth to the fridge and grabbing fingerfuls of pasta salad without using a plate or utensil. You did this. The first taste of pasta. You were not even hungry. Negative emotions along with failure take over every bit of your thought process.

You decide to hold off on your homework and head to the bathroom to shower. You have lost focus and will do it after you get out of the bathroom. What you did, without even realizing it, was leave the crime scene. You left your visual contact with the rectangular box and along with it, the potential to eat more.

I show my patients on a regular basis how to turn negative situations into positive ones. The uninvited guest in your head does not like when things are manageable or when YOU take control. It wants you to feel like crap. It wants you to feel fat. It wants you to feel like a failure. That is the tight grip it holds on you, preventing you from continuing your journey toward recovery.

By leaving the kitchen, you've taken control. Instead of doing things the old way, which would have had the strong potential of a full out binge, you walked away. As minimal or ridiculous as walking away may seem for many, this is exactly what you needed to do at that moment.

I have heard way too many stories of that exact scenario where it did not turn out okay, and the few fingerfuls of that yummy pasta dish turned into half the portion of leftovers. Eating the pasta led to a half-eaten brownie (or whatever your sister might have taken a bite out of), a handful of chips, or a spoonful of ice cream of a flavor you didn't even like; eaten right out of the container, and those two remaining chocolate candies from the Valentine candy box that no one liked. You knew no one liked them because of the fingernail marks on the bottom, and as you're chewing, you realized you didn't like the flavors either, not to mention that the pieces were as hard as a rock.

So yes, pat yourself on the back while scrubbing yourself up with your fragrant body wash in the shower. You got out; you escaped a potentially even worse scenario.

> *To avoid the above scene, do not think about that yummy pasta dish and instead try to regroup and switch that negative situation into a positive one. Return to the kitchen, grab your unfinished homework without even glancing in the direction of the rectangular box, and leave. With a clear mind, you go into your bedroom, finish that problem, and remind yourself of something I have shared with my patients.*

"Until you can be alone in the kitchen with the rectangular box, remember that the kitchen is meant to be in only while doing three things: unloading groceries, cooking, and eating."

For now, not forever, talk on the phone, do your homework, and write those invitations elsewhere. Why put yourself into a potentially hazardous situation? Have you ever heard of a recovered alcoholic reading a newspaper in a bar? Do not enter a potential crime scene without ammunition. Know where you are and what stage of recovery you are in. After all is said and done, you will be one step closer to recovery.

Your Struggle Is Real

"Entering this business, I hated being super skinny."

"Once I turned twenty-one, I started filling out a little bit, and I was loving my new curves. I appreciated having a booty."

"I am really careful if my daughter is there if I am doing photo shoots. I want to make sure that when she sees mommy in hair and makeup that she realizes that's not what's important."

— ***Christina Aguilera***
in her cover story for Health magazine 5/21

MOTHER/DAUGHTER RELATIONSHIP

In my early days of training, one of the therapy run groups was a mother/daughter group. The dynamics of the group and therapist who ran the group were amazing. As I recall one group, the conversation within holds strong feelings today, for I too have a daughter.

This group had six spots for a mom and her daughter. The therapist asked the daughters how they felt about their moms. One of the girls said that she thought her mom was amazing except when she complained about her body. Her mom was about a size 8, and at one time in her life, she was a smaller size. By today's standards of an average woman (5'4", 140 pounds, size 7 shoe, size 10 in clothes), she knew her mom wasn't fat. But, since her mom was on diet after diet and constantly asked her how she looked, this young girl often felt bad about her own body and felt disgusted if she ate anything her mom would have considered unhealthy. When her mom heard her daughter's confession, she started to tear up. She did not even realize what she was doing was negatively influencing her daughter, for it was something she did her entire life, and her older son was not affected by her dieting because he was not anorexic.

Another young lady declared that she felt ugly and hated how she looked all the time. She was anorexic and would pick at her skin or do self-harm to her face and body. When the therapist asked why she felt this way, the young girl replied, "So many people say I look like my mom, and although I think my mom is so pretty, she's constantly complaining about her looks and wants to be perfect, so when she says she needs Botox or plastic surgery on her stomach, I feel gross. If people tell me I look like my mom, then I need that too. I just want to rip my skin off or cut my stomach out."

One of the girls, 13 years old, was orthorexic (an eating disorder built on quality, not quantity of food) and without question received this style of eating from her mom who was a personal trainer and had an incredible body according to the above standards. Hearing her mom talk about healthy vs. unhealthy food almost every waking moment of her life, the daughter began to feel bad if she even had one piece of candy. As a result, she began to throw up anything she ate that her mom would have categorized as unhealthy. She said she felt better once she got that food out of her body.

As a weekly group, these kinds of revelations occurred on a regular basis, and these young girls, ages 8-13, felt safe enough in this environment to share their feelings that they had been holding back for years.

As I mentioned earlier in this chapter, I have a daughter. When I was younger and observing this group, my heart broke listening to these young girls share their feelings, but I really could not relate. Fast forward to today, and hearing my own daughter openly share her feelings with me about her body and insecurities makes me feel so grateful to have had this experience so I can guide her in a direction in a body obsessed world and teach her not to feel bad about herself.

I have never stood in front of my daughter and told her I am fat or showed her my pants and how tight they were. Even after I went through menopause and needed to throw away jeans that I knew were way too tight, I didn't discuss the fact that I had given away some of my favorite clothes with her. I just put them in a bag along with other clothes and donated them, the same as I did previously with other clothes I could not wear on a regular basis. She knows I am not the biggest fan of the wrinkles around my eyes and have likely tried every eye cream created, but there's no way I'm going to let someone stick a needle into my face for Botox injections or have plastic surgery to the point where my face isn't even me anymore. Plus, it's surgery, and the last time I checked, you can die while undergoing any form of surgery.

We do not talk about food as healthy vs. unhealthy or being good or bad. Instead, we talk about balance and finding a way to make all foods fit because of the nutrients they contain. There is no way I want my daughter to feel bad or any other negative feelings about herself in relation to the food she ate. Never. I walk around naked, and so does she (when my son is not around, of course). We do not talk about our bodies. Ever. You may think walking around naked in front of each other is crazy or disgusting, but why? What's disgusting about our naked bodies? I feel beautiful in my body with its imperfections, my varicose veins, my cellulite, and the scar from hip bone to hip bone, which is permanently left on my body from the two C-sections after giving birth to her and her brother. Have I ever pointed those things out to my daughter? No. Does she see them? I do not know. I hope she sees me, her mom, and the message she receives even if she sees those things is beauty for all those things that my body gave her, including life.

When people tell her that she is my mini me, she smiles because her thoughts of me are not just based on my looks or the size of my body. They are thoughts of pride in her mom, the one person whom she can come to when she needs to vent or talk about anything, including her body. She knows I will listen and not judge but instead help her through those really rough moments of insecurity and be there. That is your role as a mom, as a parent.

We all have moments when we feel uncomfortable in our bodies, when things we wore that we loved need to be donated because they do not fit the same. We are human, and this is part of life in a not one size fits all world. So, help your children to understand that their bodies are beautiful no matter what shape or size they are in and to also embrace the changes that it will endure with time. Embrace your body for what it does, how it helps get you from place to place and its strength to be able to do this. Believe me, your children are watching and listening to everything you are saying and doing all the time.

Your Struggle Is Real

Deb-ism #4

I used this as an acronym

F	=	False
E	=	Evidence
A	=	Appearing
R	=	Real

THE DATE

"How many calories did I just eat?"

"OK, how many can I have for a snack?"

"Damn, my boyfriend just texted me and wants to go with another couple to Chilis tonight. I have 10 more minutes of my lunch break left. Let me google what I can have."

So, you spend the next 12 minutes (10 was not enough), trying to find the exact number of calories you need and try to find a choice from a limited list. You do not even like what you chose, let alone remember the last time you liked what you ate. You ate it because it worked; it fit in your calorie counting plan.

You spend the rest of the day obsessing over what to wear and trying to remember the size that the other couple's girlfriend said she was the last time you were together. You remember that you ate crap yesterday and probably gained weight. After two more hours go by (and you have done 15 minutes of office work), you text your boyfriend, make up a white lie about your dog needing emergency surgery, and are taking him to the vet. "Sorry, I cannot go tonight. Please tell them I said hello and will look forward to next time."

Scenarios like this one are what goes on in the minds of the patients I treat. For many, the number of calories on the label or restaurant menu define their choices. Not what they would really like, what they crave, or what they are in the mood for.

When I educate my patients on picking a choice on the menu, the selection comes in a few pieces. First is the amount of time spent choosing. Yes, time. For many, the anxiety that goes into picking an actual choice without changing what their usual selection was is extremely difficult. "I'm going to order something safe. Dry, grilled chicken. I do not care what the 'special' is or that the chef developed this item based on flavor. Damn, I don't even know the last time I enjoyed my choice in a restaurant let alone tasted it. Why am I here? Right, I am on a date."

To help my patients reduce the anxiety associated with calorie counting and to help not draw negative attention to the people at the table or the waitstaff waiting to take the order, I pull out menus, time them and help them decide which choice they can make in the least amount of time. At this stage of the game, they do not need to change a food choice that is safe to a chef's special.

On the other hand, some of my patients are ready to branch out from their comfort zones. So, what is normal? How do most people choose what they would like to eat in a restaurant? First, you hear the specials. These are the chef's creations that will be fresh, for they are not regular items on the menu. Then of course there's "what am I in the mood for?" These people are ready to make the evening's choice special, especially if going out to dinner is not something they do on a regular basis. If your family is clucking from eating chicken every night, why are you ordering chicken in the restaurant?

So how could that date have turned out at Chilis? You receive a text. Feel excited that your boyfriend is taking you out and you do not have to cook. Look forward to seeing the other couple and spend the rest of your lunch break talking to your coworker about her report she needed help with. Your boyfriend shows up that evening and says you look beautiful. You thank him, and, more importantly, you feel beautiful. From the inside out. You get to Chili's. Greet the other couple. When the wait staff arrives, you order your drink, browse the menu for a minute, and make a choice. For the rest of the evening, you are present. Present in the conversation. Present in allowing yourself to taste your food choice. Present to your inner self and stop when you are full, not because you think you should based on everyone else around you. There you have it. Date at a restaurant becomes a success!

Your Struggle Is Real

"I'm not ashamed to say it out loud anymore."

— Tess Holliday
shared she's 'anorexic and in recovery'
in a recent edition of ELLE magazine

NIGHT EATING

Many of my patients ask me when the most common time of day people eat out of emotion is. To answer this question, first you need to be aware that emotional eating is not just eating when you are sad or happy; it is eating externally from your physical sensations. Outside or environmental factors always predict this style of eating.

Meeting a friend for coffee and sharing a muffin because your friend is hungry but does not want the whole thing, even though you just had dinner and are not hungry. Having breakfast before leaving for work and attending an early meeting where they are serving bagels and danish, you are only having some fruit because it is healthy, it is free, and everyone else is eating. Going to pay respects at someone's house and having a cookie because there were so many dessert type food choices and being proud of yourself that you ate only one.

Truth be told, I would ask you why you ate anything at all. Emotional eating is eating from non-hunger outside cues. It looked good, everyone else was eating, I chose something healthy, and so forth. Being mindful of "why" you are eating is the first step to awareness.

Go back to our original question asking what is the most common time people eat out of emotion? At night. After dinner. Most people find the busy structure of their day helps to tune out that inner voice of wanting something after a long time, since their last meal and their sometimes stressful day. Food, mostly snack type of food choices, is what most people choose as a reward or closure from their busy days. After dinner, after you have gone through the mail, returned the phone calls to your family, put the kids to bed, ahh, it's time to relax, and with the thought of relaxing is the thought, what do I have in the house to snack on?

Of course, it does not help if you live in the Northeast after daylight savings time when it is cold outside, all the networks on television start their series of shows in the evening, and it gets dark around 5 p.m. What else is there to do? It also does not help when you did not find enough time for breakfast that morning since you got a late start because you were helping your daughter flat iron her hair before she left for school. Or maybe skipped lunch today because you had a deadline and needed to tweak that project for review.

Believe it or not, all of those scenarios are restricting. Your body needs food (fuel) to supply energy to your brain each day, at least three times daily. When you miss a meal, even unintentionally, believe me, you are going to be searching for something later, and so the pattern, or habit, of night eating begins.

*Side note: Some of my patients have even gone as far as to develop a Sleep - Related Eating Disorder called Night Eating Syndrome (NES), whereby they wake in the middle of the night and eat or intentionally eat a large amount of food before they go to sleep. On a regular basis around 2-4 a.m., they wake up, enter the kitchen consciously or subconsciously and eat a meal.

Nocturnal Sleep Related Eating Disorder (NS-RED) involves sleepwalking with little to no recollection of doing it.

A few of my patients who have shared their food logs with me have even labeled this late night eating as breakfast. Sorry, when you have eaten three other meals that day, eating when the sun is not up is defined as NES, and as a clinician I will honestly say, is one of the hardest behaviors to get rid of.

So, you ask, how do you break this vicious cycle of constant snacking at night when you know you are not hungry? Simple. Make sure you are finding the time to have three balanced meals during the day. You find the time to brush your teeth every day. Hopefully, you bathe yourself too. Food is fuel, folks. Your body's gas. If you were running late for an appointment and had less than a quarter of a tank of gas left, wouldn't you stop to fill up? Boy, the consequence of running out of gas and having to pull over to the side of the road would, without question, make you late for the appointment for sure. Your body is similar. If you do not supply the necessary fuel for it to function properly during the day, believe me, your body will be sending out those messages later. So make the time, take the time to prepare something the night before to take to work or school. Your mind and body will be appreciative.

Your Struggle Is Real

DEBRA SPECTOR, MS, RDN, CDN

Deb-ism #5

If Diets Worked,
You Would Have Needed Only One

DAILY PLANNING AND TRIPPING UP

There is no doubt in my mind that dieting is more than a plan for weight reduction. For many, it is structure, something that will guide me and tell me what to eat for every snack and meal on a daily basis. Unfortunately, as I have said before, diets are not teaching people real life values and permanent changes.

Let us do a scenario. It is Monday. The Monday after Easter and you are determined to finally lose that five pounds you put on over the winter (as you do every winter). After going to your sister-in-law's home for Easter and eating everything not nailed down or as you told yourself driving over, have your last hoorah, you head right to the grocery store with your diet plan in hand. There, you spend over an hour scouring through the aisles for your food choices on your printed out menu from the last issue of Sports Illustrated. If those beautiful women with beautiful bodies can diet to look fabulous, so can you!

Thank goodness the store is empty, and thank goodness you are so full from all that delicious food your sister-in-law made that you are not overwhelmed by being at the grocery store and can stick to your list. How lucky are you that every item is available and driving home you have an incredible sense of relief.

After bringing the groceries in and unloading them, you change out of your clothes you wore to Easter dinner and put on something comfortable. Whew, this lounge-wear feels so much better, for those pants you were wearing felt a little snug. You head back into the kitchen and begin your preparation for Day One of your printed-out diet. Chopping, cutting, wrapping, you are ready! You head into the family room where your husband is sitting in his recliner, sit in yours, and smile. Success. You are ready.

The next morning you eat your prepared breakfast and grab your prepared-the-night-before lunch and head out the door for work. When a few coworkers bring in their "I don't want it in the house Easter candy," and you don't touch it, not even one jelly bean, fireworks go off inside of you about how proud you are of yourself for sticking to your diet. On the drive home from work, you play your favorite playlist and open your sunroof. You feel great, so in control.

You walk in the door after grabbing the mail in the mailbox and hang up your coat. After changing out of your work clothes, you head into the kitchen to start cooking your planned dinner. As you begin preparing, you get hungry. What are you supposed to do now? You already had your packed/planned snack that the diet told you to have. So you start popping cherry tomatoes into your mouth that are part of the meal prep for the salad you're making for dinner (still feeling proud that you didn't eat your kids' Easter candy that the Easter bunny left for them yesterday).

Dinner is a success, and your family compliments you on a great new meal that they would love to have again, which makes you feel even happier. You prepare Day Two lunch and snacks and head to the bathroom to wash up. As you hum in the bedroom, your husband comments about your peppy mood. Now, you are unstoppable.

Repeat the morning of Day One, except today, not only do you resist the temptation of leftover Easter candy your coworkers brought in, but also you turn down a slice of chocolate cake your coworker brought in for Susan's birthday. Heading home, you're feeling the best ever until you walk into the house and realize you forgot to defrost the chicken you purchased for Day Two dinner and need to feed the kids to get your daughter to church in an hour! You also begin to open the mail and see a bill you paid last month that you received again and need to straighten this out before their office closes at 5 p.m. So, in absolute panic mode, you do what any mom would do: you order a pizza for delivery. Thinking, you've still got control, you can have leftovers from yesterday's Day One dinner. You open the fridge and see they are missing! You text your husband who's leaving from his office in 20 minutes and he tells you he packed them for lunch, complimenting you with every bite to his coworkers on your new recipe, ugh. How can you be upset at him?

So, pizza it is, but you will only have one slice. Then, you make the billing mistake call and straighten that out. Great! The doorbell rings and the pizza delivery guy is spot on time. You feed the kids and, standing at the counter, woof down your allotted one slice of pizza that you do not even taste. Check, dinner is done.

Shuffle the kids out the door and call your husband letting him know the dinner plans are a bust, but there is a pizza on top of the stove. He is cool with that, detects your voice sounding stressed, mentions again how terrific the leftovers were from the previous night's dinner, tells you not to worry or stress over pizza.

You cannot stop thinking about the pizza, how you blew it, how upset at yourself you are about not defrosting the damn chicken, and how pissed at yourself you are for not leaving yourself a note!! How could you forget!

After dropping the kids at church, the voice in your head gets louder, and to add fuel to the fire, your stomach starts to growl. Ugh, are you kidding me! When you get home, you see your husband's car in the driveway and pray he ate the rest of the pizza. After hanging your coat up, you walk into the kitchen, and even though you know you should not, you open the pizza box. Two glorious slices left. Your stomach growls, your mouth waters, and you just grab a crust. Ok. Not so bad.

Quickly, you leave the kitchen to greet your husband and leave the two slices (one now crustless) in the box on the stove. After kissing your husband hello, you inquire about him having dinner and if he ate pizza? Yes, he replied, but only had one slice since he was still pretty full from lunch. Ugh, your leftovers. That's it! Now you're pissed off and in a funk. You head back to the kitchen because you want to stay clear of your husband and your foul mood. You don't want to pick a fight and accuse him of ruining your diet since he ate your leftovers but realize that wouldn't be a good idea.

Standing in the kitchen, you start ripping off little pieces of the crustless slice of pizza, and although it is cold and you are all alone, you begin the second slice. Now, with that little voice in your head calling you every negative word under the sun, "loser, you failed again, fat," you finish the second (really third) slice and say, "whatever." You blew it once again. Without even hesitation, you open the snack closet and start popping the kids' jelly beans into your mouth, without even tasting the sweetness of the candy. You are like an eating machine. Jellybean, pop into your mouth, chew, swallow, repeat.

Your husband calls out to you from the other room and asks if you are picking up the kids from church or do you want him to, and you snap. You see the empty pizza box and half eaten bag of jellybeans and start to cry.

You tell your husband you will go and slip the half-eaten bag of jellybeans into your pocketbook to finish on the way and off you go. No music, no sunroof open. You head out the driveway in silence. Just you and the jellybeans. And here you are, back to your old self, and it's only Day Two failure of a perfect diet.

Your Struggle Is Real

Deb-ism #6

As far as the leftover food
on your plate:
whether you eat it, throw it away,
or give it away, the food will be gone,
and you will not receive
a medal for finishing.

My closet has no medals.

JUST FOOD

Food is different for everyone, and so is eating. For some, eating is just something they do to live, or as the saying goes, they eat to live. For others, it is the center of their universe; they live to eat. Eating consists of indulging in the traditional recipes passed down from generation to generation and is what continues to hold the family together. It's the brisket on a Jewish holiday and hearing all the Jewish women compare their bubbies ('Jewish grandma's) recipes.

I love hearing my Italian friends fight over their homemade sauce recipes passed down without knowing the exact measurements for the ingredients. They simply remember their grandmas standing at the stove with her house dress on and adding a little bit of this and pinch of that, therefore never being able to get it to taste like theirs. I also love listening to them argue over what is considered sauce vs. what is considered gravy. These two scenarios stand for love of food and the true meaning behind it.

Unfortunately, for many, the memories of food are negative. These feelings could be from growing up poor and remembering how their siblings and they would count the peas on their plates to make sure everyone got the same number. Their dads made them finish all of the food on their plates because people were starving all over the world. If they did not finish it, they woke up the next day with the leftovers staring up at them for breakfast.

43

Another negative memory could be feeling overwhelmed when having steak for dinner. They received an entire steak on their plate at their grandma's homes because she was Russian and grew up in the Depression and had to use food stamps. Food became a sign of wealth that was passed down from generation to generation. The steak represented wealth, but it also had to be eaten at that meal, so they forced themselves beyond fullness to finish it to please their grandmothers and lost their abilities to know the actual feeling of fullness.

Negative memories of their parents on their new crazy diet would also exist, where instead of spaghetti with sauce at dinner, they got French green beans, for tonight, green beans are spaghetti. Or even being given a sliver of your sister's birthday cake while everyone else got a big slice because your mom says you are getting a little chunky.

For many of my patients, the negative memories hold such a strong, tight grip on them that they often ask me why they even need to eat. They feel undeserving of food and can't understand why someone in this big and creative world hasn't developed a pill to replace food. Instead, their minds are filled with negative memories or complete emptiness because the memories tend to get blocked out.

I ask my patients at their first visits to try and remember one positive memory of food being in a family environment. Most can't even recall one positive memory with food, which unfortunately is extremely common. Thankfully, some of my patients were able to remember some positive memories. A Sunday morning breakfast with the family was recalled, where their dad went out to buy their favorite bagels along with the Sunday paper, and their mom took special egg orders. Their family sat down together and spoke about their week and what lay ahead. Also, those special birthday cakes their moms baked every year were remembered. Fun family backyard barbecues with hamburgers, hotdogs, potato salad, and fresh corn after playing a game of kickball in the street together filled their minds.

Unfortunately, those positive memories are rare because most are negative. Instead, there are either no memories, for it is easier to block them out, or they are negative.

Folks, food is food. Memories are simply just memories. They do not define who you are today. Yes, we can fantasize about how differently our lives with food growing up could have been, or we can embrace where we are right now.

I will encourage you to create new, positive memories that will define who you are today. Be the new you who can have more than a sliver of cake and taste every bit of it. You can do it without judgment because you are more powerful than the cake and because you deserve the freedom from food controlling you. Believe me, you know you have arrived when you take that power away from food. It's a wonderful and empowering feeling.

Your Struggle Is Real

Deb-ism #7

Food is simply fuel for a
human gas tank.
You would not drive fifty miles with
one-fourth of a tank of gas for your
vehicle, would you?

If you did,
you would be setting
yourself up for failure
and not reach your destination.

TASTING FOOD

It is almost an everyday occurrence that I eat with my patients. The sole purpose of this activity is not to produce anxiety in my anorexic patients, lead to a binge for my patients with bulimia, or to tempt those who are compulsive overeaters, but to teach my patients how to "taste food."

Truth be told, most people are one side chewers. What does that mean? The likelihood of chewing on your right side if you are right-handed or the left side if you are left-handed is quite common. With that said, you are also most likely multitasking while eating: doing office work, opening mail, playing on any form of electronic device, watching TV or YouTube videos. In other words, you are not paying attention to what or how much you are eating and, therefore, not tasting your food.

I get it. Distraction for many of my patients helps get the food down. If I don't pay attention to the choice I'm making, the amount or why I'm eating, I can get the act of eating over with or push my feelings down or finish my homework. The bottom line is if you are not paying attention, you are not tasting your food either.

Your tongue is a muscle that has thousands of taste buds on it. Certain areas of your tongue detect assorted flavors. Sweet, salty, bitter, acidic, metallic are just a few to name. Those of you who are one side chewers are not tasting your food, and feeling unsatisfied, you either keep eating or just do not enjoy what you have eaten.

Something else to make a mental note of is the fact that many of my patients eat too quickly. I am sure some of you do too. Combine that with not really tasting what you chose to eat, and there you have it, two situations put together that either:

1. Make you feel like you did not eat because you ate too quickly, or
2. You did not even taste the choices you made.

Have you ever noticed the last time you ate one chip, you have wanted and eaten more? Did you notice that you did not taste them after the first one? Think harder about that memory. What were you doing while you were eating those chips? Were you doing paperwork? Watching a movie? Talking to your cousin at a backyard family get together? Now, try to remember how many you ate. When did you stop? Did you stop because the allotted portion you gave yourself ran out? Did you stop because another cousin called you over at the backyard party where she was standing, and there were no chips where she was standing? Now think again; did you taste what you ate?

At this exact point is when the mental babble begins. All the uncertainty. How much did I eat? From there comes the compensation for the food choices you make later that day.

Remember, we can find pleasure and enjoy the foods we choose. We are deserving of that satisfaction. So, try it. Pay attention. Taste the food you choose to eat and embrace one of the wonderful senses meant to be honored.

Your Struggle Is Real

"I wish I had a better metabolism, but someone else probably wishes they could walk into a room & make friends with anyone like I can."

— *Kelly Clarkson*
An American singer who rose to fame for winning the first season of American Idol in 2002

MINDFULNESS

In our hurried world where there is never enough time in a day, we, unfortunately, lose sight of so many wonderful things going on around us. People are so busy with their electronics, they do not realize they are missing the wonders of our world: the sky, nature, and, most importantly, our loved ones.

As always, I am a firm believer in mindfulness. Not looking back, for that can likely cause depression. Do not look too far ahead because projection can lead to anxiety. In my practice, I find way too often, my patients eat at their desks while looking at their computers or cell phones. My patients in high school are shunned for having a lunch period and are pushed to take an extra class and, therefore, forced to eat in an academic class. Because of these things, they miss many of the pleasures that mindful eating brings us... taste, flavor, texture, and temperature with usually instead a feeling of dissatisfaction and quite often overeating.

Positive lifestyle changes can feel like a chore; they are too hard to make permanent. The problem most people have is they resolve to change something that is too hard to do permanently or resolve to change too many things and cannot manage all of them. As a Registered Dietitian Nutritionist, I teach permanent, forever change. It is okay to take two steps forward and sometimes one step back when we feel like that one step is too hard for right now. The key component is that we are always ahead.

So, try your best to choose something you feel needs enough attention to change and really give it a go. If you feel like you have failed, get up, wipe the dust off, and keep moving forward. Remember that you are a few steps ahead of where you were. As humans, we are adaptable. Stress reduction, mindfulness, meditation, good sleep, a balanced diet where all foods fit, body movement that is attainable, and fluids. Simple yet way too hard for many.

With this said, I encourage all of you to try to eat mindfully. I promise, the ten minutes taken to eat a sandwich won't compromise that text that could wait to be returned, that "like" on Facebook or other social media, and, more importantly, you may enjoy what you are eating.

Awareness is a powerful tool, so give it a shot. Put your phone down, close your laptop, and look out the window or at the person sitting right in front of you. Believe me, as a firm believer and someone who practices mindfulness every day, I assure you that you will not believe what you have been missing!

Your Struggle Is Real

Deb-ism #8

I've Been On A Diet For Two Weeks And All I've Lost Is 14 Days.

THE SCALE

How is it even possible to allow a non-emotional object to take control of your emotions? To allow it to make you feel good or bad about yourself? Let us break down one piece of this identity for some of my patients to prove to you that there is no value in it: the number on the scale. Almost daily, I need to supply proof, evidence that the number you see flashing up at you is just that... a number.

You know the scale has really taken on a different meaning when it controls your life choices or events for the day. What if you get on the scale, you have been doing well on your journey of eating (in your mind), and you have gained weight? Does whatever you have later that day change? You had a date with that special someone who chose to ask you out and because you gained three fourths of a pound, you are cancelling. Or you weigh yourself, and the number is the same. All that exercise you did yesterday didn't work, so why bother ever exercising again, or you say, I'm going to have to add on an extra hour now. You have a get together with friends and the number that flashed back that morning was too high, so you find an excuse to skip the get together. If the number were lower than expected and upon going to the office, you found out you were not one of the employees being laid off, but it would not matter because to you, success is the fact that the number on the scale went down.

Many, if not most, of my patients have an actual fear of being weighed. They are ashamed of the number. Although I can guess anyone's weight within five pounds, the truth is I need to get a weight on record. Almost always I weigh my patients "blind" or backwards. Most often taking their height and weight at the same time. Why put someone on this terrifying piece of machinery more than once? Many of my patients have a deeper fear of their friends or family finding out how much they weigh than they do of me knowing the number. More times than not, I ask parents or spouses to step into the waiting room while I weigh my patient. Although their weight is "just a number," for many they use this number as a measure of success or failure. It defines their identity and, along with that, their mood.

I try to help my patients understand that when you weigh yourself one to four times per day or more, weighing yourself all the time becomes a behavior. Usually the number will be the same within a five pound range when you compare the number you see at the same time of day you weigh yourself. Getting on and off, sometimes more than once daily, makes or breaks their moods, their self-worth, their success, or, unfortunately, their failure.

Fact: your body is made up of a lot of water and prone to hydration shifts. Salty foods, binging on carbohydrates, humidity, menstruation, even the cabin pressure in an airplane can change the fluid in your body, thereby changing the number you see on the scale.

Fact: you cannot write on a college application or Linked In profile, My name is: "your name," and I weigh 99 pounds and am a size 0. They would likely shred your application, for having that information as your identity is not the most important achievement. The number on the scale and the size you wear in clothes is real, yes, it is, but it does not define your full identity. It is a part of you, but not the whole you.

So many of my patients use this electronic piece of machinery to define who they are. Part of getting better is reducing the behavior of weighing yourself often and trusting yourself while forming your identity.

Who are you? A writer, painter, student, parent? What peaks your interests? Nature, spirituality, animals, volunteering, decorating? What is of value to you that has nothing to do with food, weight, or body image?

Our bodies have a set point weight. A weight where it "wants to be." I help my patients to accept this as a more valuable range, usually within five pounds as I mentioned before.

Own the number on the scale and the size you're in. Accept it. Embrace it. Live your life and do not give up what could become wonderful memories because of a number. More importantly, be mindful of those other unique parts of you and wonderful things that make you special besides the number on an electronic piece of equipment.

Your Struggle Is Real

"I'm not asking you to like my body.
I'm just asking you to let me be me.
Because I'm going to influence a girl who does look like me,
and I want her to feel good about herself."

— Serena Williams
on body image, in the September issue of Self magazine

THE NEW AMERICAN TEEN

Being an adolescent or teenager in the 21st century is, without question, much more difficult than it was when I was younger. When I was a kid growing up, we felt the same social pressures. Having the right haircut, wearing Jordache jeans, carrying the "in" backpack, and hanging with the popular kids.

Although that commonality is present today, the significant difference is when we left school when we were younger, we did just that - left school. In present times there is social media: Instagram, SnapChat, Finsta accounts, Facebook, Tik Tok, You Tube videos. Our kids are beyond connected, and because of this disconnect, they do not know how to relax, reload, and recharge. Our kids are not turning off. They are not leaving those pressures behind.

Kids in Intermediate School have cell phones or even younger ages than that have Tablets. Are you kidding me? Why does an 8-year-old need a cell phone? For the one emergency per year that they need to reach you? You should have taught them how to do that long before you gave them a cell phone. Parents are so busy either living vicariously through their kids and overcompensating for what they missed out on growing up or doing the complete opposite and not seeing the bigger picture.

Wake up, folks! Your adolescents and teenagers are not your friends. Do your job and teach your kids how to relax, reload, and recharge. Our schools are not doing this for you. They are part of the problem. Not having a lunch period, being forced to eat in class while listening to your teacher and the entire time worrying if anyone is hearing you chew. Or even worse, not eating and trying to focus while struggling to make it through the day because a granola bar was the only thing that they were able to eat today between 5:30 a.m. and 5:30 p.m. We need to join forces, parents. Let's advocate for our kids and be their voices.

Believe me, as a RDN in private practice in the community I see the bigger picture. Kids ages eight and up are on medicine for anxiety, OCD, and depression. The number of referrals for me to see your kids who suffer from eating disorders is at a record high. Please. Please. Help to be a voice. Your kids are exhausted, stressed, and overwhelmed.

Our generation had lunch daily. Most of us have higher education degrees and have jobs that support us to live on Long Island. We were forced to relax, reload, and recharge. Shame on the Board of Education for not advocating for our kids. We are a force. Use your skills and knowledge to help make this happen, just like I am doing.

Your Struggle Is Real

Deb-ism #9

You never realize
how capable of change you are
until you need to be capable.

PERMANENT CHANGE

Every day a new healthy food comes out on the market. Every day someone is diagnosed with Type II diabetes. Sadly a few of those diagnosed will be nine-and-ten-year-old children.

We all have a blueprint. Genetically speaking, we cannot change this blueprint, and it makes up 50% of who we are as humans. Thankfully, the other 50% is environmental. What that means is, you have control of the things outside of your internal blueprint. You have control of sleep and how much you get, including the quality of it. You control the amount of fluids you take in and the type you choose, body movement (some call it exercise) and how often you schedule it in. Lastly, you have control of your food choices, in both quality and quantity.

I have seen a lot over the last thirty-one years while working in my private practice: children as young as eight who throw up their food as well as a thirteen-year-old who weighed over five hundred pounds. Shocked, I am sure, you need to understand that these children have learned these behaviors. They are not genetic. How and where could they have learned them? My eight-year-old patient's older sister was bulimic, and just living in the same household as her, most of the family discussion was around her sister throwing up or not, and she received a lot of attention. My patient, therefore, learned how to throw up on YouTube. My thirteen-year-old patient, had a very absentee Mom, who was on every diet, talked about food most of her waking moment, and had only junk food in the house for their grandparents so, it was off limits to my patient who was told this on a regular basis. She would eat this type of food uncontrollably at her friend's house and/or sneak her grandparents' snacks at her house when her mom was out. Believe me, she knew the exact time her mom was coming home. Unfortunately, her binge eating led to Type II diabetes at thirteen.

Interesting enough, these four environmental factors (sleep, fluids, body movement, and food) are the most constant aspects of human metabolic function, but by far, the hardest to sustain. Strangely enough, in my practice, it is a constant hardship on the patients' part to consistently keep up with those four factors.

In my opinion, Western medicine is failing us. Truth be told, I have seen the result too many times of people taking only prescription medicine without controlling those four factors for health and wellbeing. Yes, it is hard, and yes, the change needs to be permanent, lasting forever. I will tell you from firsthand experience, the payoff will be the best you have ever received.

Why is it that people can put the time and effort into education, receiving degree after degree or into a sport, practicing day after day, but foolishly believe any consistent effort to their health and wellbeing isn't as important?

Underneath all of their trappings, the richest people in the world or the highest paid football players are still human. They still have the same responsibilities to take care of themselves to improve their quantity as well as quality of life. Do you know anyone who says in their early days, "I'm going to achieve all I want and not live long enough or well enough to reap the benefits of my challenging work and effort?" I know I do not.

Americans are so on and off; they are missing the bigger picture.

Fact: Diets are temporary. When was the last time you heard a friend say they went on one and followed it at her sister in law's house on Thanksgiving? When was the last time you did not make an excuse (just this one last time) and finish the box of cookies that your kids opened because, you're never going to eat cookies again. Ever? Do you know people who bring their packaged food on their cruise to the Caribbean? How about counting points while at a wedding? Drinking their protein shake for breakfast while vacationing in Italy? I highly doubt it. These are the times when most people are off and convince themselves that this is okay.

If you think for one fleeting moment that your kids are not watching you and following in your footsteps as far as your relationship with food, weight, and body image, you are obviously either not paying attention or clueless!

Most of your beliefs about food and exercise stem from your childhood home environment. If your mom cooked dinner every night and served each family member a plate at the stove because she made "just enough" for everyone, you will do the same with your kids. If your dad sat in his recliner every night after dinner and snacked, although you knew he was not hungry since he just finished dinner an hour ago, you would think this practice to be normal. Whatever message about body image that was a constant in your family growing up will most often carry into your adulthood. If your mom constantly stood in front of a mirror and commented negatively about her body ("ugh, these jeans are so tight, I feel so fat, I must fit into that dress this Friday night.

I cannot eat breakfast until then"), believe me, you were listening. The important message I want you to receive is to be mindful of what your environmental message delivers in your house as far as food, weight, and body image are concerned. As my own Mom often said, "Little pitchers have big ears." For those of you who never heard that expression: your children are watching as well as listening.

Your Struggle Is Real

"I'm actually heavier than I was three years ago,
but I accept my body as it is today.
I work out not to lose weight but to maintain my good health."

—Ashley Graham*,*
on body shaming comments she received after posting
a photo of herself looking slimmer on "Lenny Letter."

THE SNACK TABLE

Whenever I go over to my Aunt Clara's house, it blows me away how each room in her house has something tasty to snack on. The living room has a candy dish, which always has the latest holiday treat: pink and white M&Ms for Valentine's Day, jellybeans for Easter, red and green Hershey kisses for Christmas, etc. What really amazes me is how we all know the room with the plastic couch coverings was off limits, but we all constantly sneaked in not only to get a glimpse of what new sweet and tasty treat she has displayed, but also to grab a handful. How do I know what they did? Because I often saw my cousins unwrapping something and popping it into their mouths, plus before I head home, I had a ritual of checking the bowl to see how much has disappeared.

Fast forward 30 years. Even though the candy dish still supplies its own magical entity, the thing that brings the most attention to me is her snack table, which is strategically placed in her den. The den is where everyone hangs out, the room not off limits where the TV and comfy seating are. To see that much snack type food produces so much anxiety in me that I not only have a tough time entering the room, but also I have a challenging time staying in there for more than five minutes at a time.

When I am in the room, I watch my family constantly go over

to the snack table to grab a handful of whatever tasty snack they would like: chips, not one, but three types, tortilla chips with salsa, cheese and crackers, goldfish crackers for my younger cousins. My aunts and uncles eat these goodies too. There is so much crunching that the sound is drilled into me. The room smells like salt and grease. It makes me nauseous.

My cousin Madison asks me to sit down on the couch so we can talk. I reluctantly sit but find myself distracted by the constant movement toward the snack table. I am having a really challenging time staying present in the conversation. Then, I hear my older cousin Michelle tell my cousin Barbara that she is on a diet. The latest and greatest one. After explaining for all to hear what that is, I can feel my heart beating out of my chest, so loudly that I wonder if anyone else can hear it. After her explanation of what her diet entails, Barbara tells her she's crazy and she should just follow the "2 rule." Eat two of whatever you want. Michelle wanted to get a better understanding of what she was talking about, and in all honesty, so did I.

At this point, Madison realizes I am not listening to her and begins eavesdropping on the other conversation and stops talking altogether. "The eat two rule was taught to me by my personal trainer. What you do is decide what you are in the mood for and give yourself permission to eat two of that choice. Let's be honest, she says, you don't taste more anyway. Usually you do not realize it, but you taste the first and last of whatever you have eaten. The ones in the middle are the you-blew-it-anyway chips, etc. and the troublemakers."

Finally, Aunt Clara calls us into the dining room for dinner, and I sit in disbelief and watch my family eat again, after snacking on lots of food. I even wonder if they are hungry. But mostly, I spend the rest of the night mulling over what my cousin Barbara said and want to learn more of what her personal trainer said that I do not even remember eating or what the conversation was at the dinner table.

Because I am not going to be the one to ask Barbara more and draw attention to myself, the conversation is over. But, without even being conscious of it, I become extremely hyper-focused on her. Watching her eat through dinner, it appeared to me she was eating enough and simply fine, but this observation is coming from me, someone who is completely clueless on how to judge her own amount of food to be eaten at every given time.

After dinner, we all help clean up. You guessed it. I stay in the kitchen washing dishes, far away from the room with the snack table. As my family is bringing the bowls of tasty crunchy things into the kitchen to clear them away, Aunt Clara declares she doesn't want to throw them away and asks us to please put them in Ziploc storage bags so she can have them for her Mahjong card game.

My cousins respond and do just that, and I hear crunching and chewing noises behind me. Obviously, they did not hear or understand Barbara's two chip rule. They said they were full from dinner, so why are they eating snacks now? When we are washing dishes, I try to recall what they ate at dinner and then try to think back to what they ate when we were together. This reflectionary period lasts longer than I would like.

And there you have it, the end of what could have been an amazing gathering with family that became all about the snack table. Suddenly, you realize the time and say your goodbyes. On the way out though, of course, you peek into the forbidden room because rituals are just that: rituals. As expected, the candy bowl is 1/3 of the way full compared to what it looked like when I arrived.

The ride home is filled with chatter about the entire evening, but mostly the snack table. With it is the simple fact that the snack table once again wins, for it took away the true meaning of why I got together with my family in the first place.

Your Struggle Is Real

OLDER PATIENTS

First, understand that it is extremely rare that I get a new patient with the onset of an eating disorder at an old age. Honestly, if they have an eating disorder much later in life, they have been keeping their thoughts bottled up for an exceptionally long time. Can you even imagine reaching a time in your life when the only health issue you have is an eating disorder?

You do not have the energy to work because your cognitive function has declined. You do not have the ability to live on your own because you cannot take care of yourself or find the energy to clean your house, so you need to live with your aging parents. You cannot own a pet because you cannot remember to feed it daily and do not have enough energy to take it out for a walk or change the litter box/cage.

The love you have is bottled up and reserved for only one. Your eating disorder. You cannot be in a healthy relationship with anyone because every waking moment and thought is spent on food, weight, and body image. By this age, and by doing this for an extended period of time, you are exhausted.

Many of my older patients wish that someone, anyone, would have alerted them to where they would be now if they did not find help at a younger age. Unfortunately, many of them tried to get help, but reached out to the wrong people who encouraged them to eat healthy or yes, losing another five pounds in their stomachs would be a great idea. For those who received this message, the beginning to no end had begun just like that. Before they knew it, their self-worth and self-esteem were based on validation about the choice of food they made or how they looked. Food, weight, and body image became their identity and what defines them and their success.

To me, my patients who walk in my office at any age are courageous. Change is hard at any age, but change at an older age, in my mind, is the hardest when you have been using your behaviors for decades and cannot imagine doing it another way or giving them up. For those of you brave enough to begin this journey, good for you! You should be immensely proud of yourself and your strength. Your "future self" will thank you.

Your Struggle Is Real

Deb-ism #10

Body image is the
bookends of recovery.
It is usually the first to come
and the last to leave.

ABSOLUTE PERFECTION

Fact: Food, weight, and body image are women's issues of the 21st Century, especially in America. People here are obsessed with their bodies and changing them to meet the expectations of the media and what it perceives as reality, when in essence, it is not. No one has a perfect body. Never did. Most people can only achieve what they consider perfection by controlling, manipulating, and doing anything possible to get there.

I just want thinner thighs, a flatter stomach, to lose five more pounds. Plastic surgery, Botox, fillers...what will it take to make you perfect? Once you begin the desire for absolute perfection by using these extremes, most will find that it is never enough. What else can I improve? How can I get there? So, you read, Google, and read blogs for the answer until you realize you have lost complete control.

The obsession with food, weight, and body image has taken over your life. Every free second and moment of the day becomes mind babble, actual dialog.

When I was a young girl, my Dad was a photographer. He photographed models, and back then, he would take pictures the old-fashioned way with a camera and then develop them. He often told me about some of these women and how challenging it was to remove the cellulite in their photos. Well, fast forward to today and I am sure you recognize that times have changed. Now, anyone can photoshop, edit, and change the lighting in a photo to reveal perfection. No one looks like absolute perfection in real life. No one.

I remember in my early days of training and working with eating disorders at The Center for Managing Eating Disorders on Central Park West. The office received a phone call, and I was asked to do an interview on Good Day New York about "How to prevent overeating during the Holidays" on Thanksgiving Day. That was 1994, but I remember that day like it was yesterday. My five minutes of fame. So, I woke up at dawn, found a suitable suit for television, and did my make up to my standards. Off I went, feeling nervous and excited.

Once I arrived, the people who worked in the studio brought me to "makeup" because my standard was way below theirs and put so much makeup under my eyes to cover my apparent dark circles that I never realized were that dark. Then, those same people led me to the Green Room where I was to await my interview. With all the hustle and bustle around me, I was astonished to see so many people this early in the day transformed into what appeared as a "new self." When I was finally called in, I was so happy to see I was being interviewed by a lead news caster. After the people who worked in the studio brought me in, sat me down, and positioned me, I was greeted by him. I was amazed that a man could wear that much makeup. Quite honestly, and call me naive if you would like, I did not even realize men wore makeup on TV. After all, it was the 90's.

Fast forward to today. Makeup, hair, lighting, special effects and then photoshop. Voila, perfection; but not reality.

73

Also, fast forward to today and spend time educating your children on how people spend way too much time and money to achieve absolute perfection before you buy them a cell phone and they join every social media account and start judging themselves with all those photos that have been manipulated to perfection. If you do not think they are looking at social media accounts, you're delusional. It is, right now, in the other room, your 9-year-old is looking at other peoples accounts and with that, comparing themselves to others that they see.

Now, look back. Why is it that we all look so different? How come my girlfriend is so much taller than me? Has the most incredibly shaped eyes? Looks amazing in a short dress because she has the longest legs without varicose veins? But when you get to know this friend, all she talks about is her plastic surgery appointment in two months to remove "fat on her arms" because she feels like she's got arms like her grandma that jiggle when she waves goodbye; therefore, she will never wear a sleeveless top or even worse, a tank top. Her surgery date was meticulously chosen based on the weather and days left at work for her PTO (Personal Time Off). You see, she is going to recreate herself and be perfect.

This type of story happens on a regular basis. Confidence that comes from the outside/in. I am not trying to "sell you" on the fact that we should not look good, not get our hair cut, dress according to the dress attire at the events you attend, bathe, brush our teeth, even choose a piece of jewelry that was a special hand-me-down from past generations. But, plastic surgery, Botox, fillers? When will the insanity of trying to achieve absolute perfection stop? When will all of these drastic measures to achieve this perfection be good enough? Fillers and Botox will change your appearance, but once they wear off, and they will, you will need to do them again. Do more; intoxicating they can become like a drug. Plastic surgery is a type of surgery, and as with all surgeries it has its risks.

I know that this obsession can get out of control. I am sure you have seen the tales of fillers and Botox stories on the news. Super stars get plastic surgery to appear younger and completely transform themselves into someone we cannot recognize. Then, there are the stories we have heard about plastic surgeries that are so over the top an obsession they led to death. Unfortunately, I know a few of them. So sad.

Of course, I cannot tell you what to do. I can only bring awareness to a subject worth bringing attention to. I can ask you to pause, educate yourself. Be aware of the risks involved and the truth behind them. Any decision in life is a decision. Just make sure it is a good one. As the old saying goes, "It's working smarter, not harder that leads to the best decisions."

Your Struggle Is Real

*"We all have cellulite, even supermodels.
I've been to fashion shows and seen it! It's nature.
Without it you aren't human."*

— *Sandra Bullock*
An Academy Award actress and producer

WEIGHT AS A BARRIER

Many people of larger size use their weight to cover up many things. This shell of protection is used as a barrier against the outside world as well as the scary parts of it, mostly trauma and often sexual abuse.

The opposite holds true for many of my patients with anorexia. Think about it, when your curves are gone, you lose your menstruation, and your breasts are small enough for a training bra or you don't need to wear one at all, you feel you are not so appealing to the opposite sex and, therefore, safe. Some have even gone as far to say this look closely mimics the body of a little boy.

Many of my patients have used these barriers to the outside world as a means to keep them safe. Until they can find the strength and courage to move past the trauma, most stop treatment or hit a pause button. Many must work in unison with a skilled and trained therapist who specializes in trauma and even benefit from EMDR (eye movement desensitization and reprocessing).

The feeling of fullness is also an extremely uncomfortable feeling, and for many of my patients, the use of laxatives or purging is what they use to assist in helping them to feel empty and provide relief from that full feeling. Again, they need to be ready to accept what the feeling of fullness is to begin the process of recovery.

For me, a patient needs also to embrace the internal sensations of hunger and fullness so I can assist them with intuitive eating and appetite regulation, which are two key components of eating disorder recovery. I have developed a technique that many of my patients who have struggled with trauma have found helpful in assisting in developing these internal mechanisms so we can begin this process in a delicate non-intrusive way. I teach this population to be in touch with their hunger from the outside/in. As a result, most of my patients who are gently taught this approach are successful, and with that positive attribute they begin a window of opportunity to help them slowly engage in appetite regulation as well as hunger awareness with a safety cushion.

So, the next time you see someone of an enormous size or the complete opposite, of a tiny size, be mindful of what you say. Too many times, my patients report back to me that their doctor and/or pediatrician will make insensitive statements alluding to the fact that they need to lose or gain weight without completely understanding the big picture. Before you say something, ask a few questions. Don't be judgmental. This person has feelings and will likely react in some way. All it takes is a little patience and understanding to get the full picture. If you're not trained to specialize in eating disorders, encountering someone who has one gives you an opportunity to recommend someone who is.

In all honesty, many of my patients begin treatment with me as a result of words said to them from their doctors, coaches, clergy, and so forth. In my mind, these people are often emulated by my patients as the most respectful person in their lives, so those words are golden and often become their new identity or lack of.

I use education and focus on health and wellbeing as a teaching tool as well as a mechanism to provide evidence-based information to my patients. This method often challenges the deep-rooted beliefs and rituals they have developed that aren't based on factual information. I find it not uncommon for my patients to actually believe that their rituals are real. We all know there is a fine line between perception and reality. As a clinician, I find it my responsibility to help my patients understand the difference and develop new beliefs that are evidence based. When this shift begins to happen, the eating disorder (the "uninvited guest") loosens its tight grip, and new, factual behaviors begin.

Sensitivity and listening closely, often with a third ear (listening in order to understand rather than listening in order to respond) is the best advice I can offer.

Sometimes they just want to be heard. Really be heard. As much as we can often be judgmental and want to rescue or provide help, timing is often the most essential piece with this highly sensitive and fragile population.

Your Struggle Is Real

Deb-ism #11

Confidence is Sexier
Than A Size Zero.

STOMACH SURGERY

I get calls to my office on a regular basis, sometimes weekly, from people who find me in their insurance website and need a consult letter as part of the protocol to have some form of Bariatric surgery: Gastric Bypass, Sleeve Gastrectomy, Gastric Banding, Gastric Balloon. I'm sure they will create another name by the time this book is published.

I used to provide them years ago. I am sure like other medical providers do because these patients need other consults to have this operation. Then it hit me, yes, I can type up a consult letter for this person I really do not know much about, or I can help them, guide them to get a better understanding as to why they need the surgery in the first place.

Truth be told, you do not just wake up one day one-hundred pounds overweight. That weight gain did not happen overnight. I am sure there are many contributing factors to what led you to this place. It was a disservice to write a consult letter for someone I did not really know. Side note: If any of my existing patients, whom I have gotten to know, decide that this would be the best choice and even though they have lost weight or are left with over 100 pounds remaining, I have no problem writing them a consult note.

For others, I suggest they begin seeing me and let's discover together what caused this excessive weight to be present. Have they been binge eating? Emotionally overeating? Perhaps they have NES, night eating syndrome (see chapter on night eating), and do not even realize they have it. Let us be honest, as the old saying goes, you cannot put a bandaid on an open wound that needs stitches.

So, our journey begins. It is enlightening for me to guide these people gently in a direction where they have never been before. Yes, most have been on countless diets, and failure after failure have ended up in this place where, at their wits end, they have decided it is the only choice.

A handful of these people have successfully taken off weight along with learning some life lessons about their relationship with food and conquered some of their biggest fears and made permanent changes, which take quite a bit of courage and self-discipline. A few of these patients have lost over 100 pounds with my guidance and opted out of taking this drastic measure of going under the knife. Instead, they have faced their issues that have brought them here in the first place (usually with the collaboration of a therapist).

To be able to cross your legs while sitting in a chair again, wear a lace up shoe because all you were able to wear before this weight loss was a slip on. To go to a concert or baseball game and not have anxiety before sitting down about whether you will fit in the seat or not. To be able to fit through a turnstile at Disney World with your four-year-old, or even better, to fit in a seat on the airplane that takes you there, without a seatbelt extender or to have to pay for an extra seat on the airplane. These are just a few milestones these brave people get to do that most average weight people don't even think about.

Our world and the choices available to us will make many of us question ourselves and the decisions we make. As much as the choice to have Bariatric surgery is an individual decision, think long and hard, for this is surgery. Remember, with any surgery you sign a waiver that points out risks, one of which is death. I understand you have unsuccessfully tried every diet and the likelihood of regaining all the weight you had lost in the past is back and with all your attempts you have reached this decision.

Most people cannot relate to the consequences of being in a large body. The feeling of having extremely large breasts and having to put powder underneath them after you shower to prevent them from rubbing, having your legs chafe from walking, or having fat hang over on your stomach and, therefore, having your pants and/or belt placed above or below your stomach for comfort. Many of my patients who come to me after the surgery are left with skin hanging down or a girdle of skin left after losing a significant amount of weight (usually after Bariatric surgery) and will need plastic surgery (yes, more surgery) to remove it. A few of my patients have told me horrific stories of getting a staph infection on the underpart of their skin because keeping it clean and dry can be extremely difficult.

Before the surgery, see a RDN who specializes in eating disorders if only a few times to hear a unique perspective. For me personally, to see these brave people engage in new behaviors along with many positive life changes makes me immensely proud of their continued efforts. To have them begin to see themselves as successful rather than a failure will, without doubt, be a forever mood booster with each life changing decision.

Your Struggle Is Real

"I'm prouder of my weight loss than my Oscar!"

— *Jennifer Hudson*
on dropping from a size 16 to a 6 in Self magazine

BODY MOVEMENT

With temperatures hitting almost seventy-five degrees, this weekend begins the babble (if it hasn't already begun). "Damn I have to put shorts on, a sleeveless top, or even worse a bathing suit. I have not worked out in months. What is wrong with me! I promised myself I would stick to my gym routine after January 1st. I do not even remember the last time I had time to exercise, and I hate working out! Ugh, fine. I will go to the gym after work today." So, with good intentions, you pack your gym bag before you head to the train and off you go. At 3:30 p.m., your boss calls an emergency meeting, and yes, you guessed it, another night you are going to have to skip the gym.

Fact: You do not need to do body movement every day. When you set yourself up with too grand expectations, as I have said way too many times, you are setting yourself up to fail. It is extremely difficult with the demands of today's society to keep and, more importantly, continue with a goal like that forever. Exercise is even more on and off by nature than meeting your nutritional goals.

Fact: You are in a human body. It is your responsibility to move it, take loving care of it, and help your blood to circulate through your heart, your lungs, and your organs. Getting your heart rate up ensures that you are doing your part to guarantee that you are making a "forever" effort at achieving a responsibility that only

85

you can take part in. So, stop making excuses and get going! We only need to move and get our heart rates up two to four times per week for 30-60 minutes. That is the "forever" goal. So, as I ask my patients to do each week, look at your hectic schedule and find a way to fit in three days. This way, when that emergency meeting occurs, and you only get in two that week, you have achieved your goal and feel really good about yourself. Win-win.

My message: please set realistic, attainable goals. Your body and your mind will love you for it!

Your Struggle Is Real

A MUCH NEEDED
MOTIVATIONAL COLLECTION

Where you are now...today...at this moment isn't the result of what you've done recently, yesterday, or likely a week ago. Who you are and what makes you tick has actually evolved from years of use and even possibly abuse.

We are humans, not robots. Change is hard. Life is not as simple as changing a battery in an electronic device and forgetting about it as it doesn't require much attention anymore and will most likely not require attention until the next time you need to change its battery.

With that said, with all the months and possibly years of wiring our brains to work a certain way, why do we have expectations of quick results when we decide to make those changes we've set out to do? My daughter's wedding is in two months, and I need to go down two dress sizes to fit into my dress. I told the store to order me a size 12. I've been following my diet and cheated only once at my cousin's party, and that wasn't as bad as I could've been. How come I didn't lose weight?

Wow, we sure have high expectations of ourselves to see results pretty quickly. As most of my followers know, I'm not a sugar coater. I'm not going to sell you on a quick journey or a one stop fits all answer.

I will remind you that everything worthwhile you've ever achieved didn't occur overnight, in a day, a month, and often not in a year: your college degree, from conception to the birth of your child, establishing credit to purchase your first home.

The message I'm hoping you receive from me today is to slow down, keep moving forward, and lower your expectations. Think of a footbridge, a wobbly scary bridge that sometimes, if it's really long, you can't see the end of. When you walk on it, it gets shaky. You grab hold of the ropes in fear of falling. The end is unclear, not in your view. You know that turning back is not an option anymore, for you've done that before and it doesn't serve you anymore. So, you keep moving forward. Step after step, day after day, however long it takes. When you get to the end and you look back at that bridge, you will have achieved something you can be proud of for your entire life, and, believe me, in time, you won't even remember how difficult the journey was!

So breathe and keep it moving forward. You've got this.

Your Struggle Is Real

"I heard my body is a topic of conversation so I wanted to say,
I'm proud of my body and you should be proud of yours too...
Be you and be relentlessly you.
That's the stuff of champions."

— ***Lady Gaga***
on comments made about her
during her performance in Super Bowl 2017.

SUMMER

Summer has finally arrived, and I am sure with the long, sunny days, all of you have had a lift in mood and spirit. This seasonal return often brings a reminder to many people, and to my patients, it's bathing suit season and along with that, especially for people with poor body image and body preoccupation, comes anxiety.

Reminder: food, weight, and body image are issues of the 21st century. They are not going away any time soon. Learning to understand or cope with these issues will help improve your quality of life.

For some of my patients, the thought of putting on a bathing suit produces so much anxiety, they would rather socially isolate or wear clothes to cover up the part or parts of their bodies they are not too fond of. Sadly, for many, that is everything besides their head, hands, or feet.

I am sure many of you feel this way whether conscious or subconscious. Body size acceptance is extremely important. I often say to my patients, "We are human, we have imperfections, and we come in all different shapes and sizes. This is not a one size fits all world."

The population of my patients who struggle the most are adolescents and teenagers. In their world, there is constant comparison with Snapchat, Instagram, Tik Tok, and many other forms of social media.

What are some of the things, among many, that I teach my patients to do so they may switch their channels? We all have parts of our bodies we love and other parts that we don't so much. This is reality when it comes to body image acceptance. So, instead of scheduling an appointment for plastic surgery and taking a risk on your life, I suggest emphasizing the parts you love and deemphasizing the parts you do not love as much. What a much better choice than feeling the need to walk outside in bubble wrap or spend the summer in front of the fourth season of your favorite reality show. Something else I often say is to remind yourself, in this not one size fits all world, that there are all different kinds of bathing suits for all different kinds of body shapes for a reason; we are all shaped differently. Bikinis, tankinis, one piece, high waisted, speedo, board shorts, tops with push up bras, tops that look like tube tops, bottoms with skirts, thong bottoms, and so forth, all have a specific purpose and body shape in mind.

Living on Long Island provides many benefits, one of which is enjoying our beaches. Last season, I asked a friend who, in my mind, has poor body image to join me. How can I be so sure she has bad body image? What makes me arrive at that decision? Several things, such as when you are tiny in size by nature and decide to have plastic surgery to fix a part of your body. In my friend's example, it was breast implants. Side note: breast implants are the number one request for graduation gifts for teenage girls which sadly their parents are giving them. After having them done, my friend decided breast implants weren't enough and showed me, while in her bikini, how the fat rolled over the back of her bikini bottom and needed to be removed.

Obviously, body dissatisfaction has become a huge dilemma in the States. I always declare that if I were a RDN in Europe, I would starve. Americans have issues, while Europeans feel comfortable enough to go to the beach topless, naked, and in Speedo bathing suits. No matter how far down their breasts sag, their stomach flab hangs over their bathing suit bottoms, or how hairy their armpits and legs are, they still enjoy the beach without breast implants or waxed/lasered hair removal. Good for them! As a majority, they don't have poor body image, and the lack of it frees their minds for more wonderful things to fill their lives with, such as the enjoyment of friends or family they are with, the sunshine, the ocean, nature, or the many other special joys surrounding them that don't have to do with body dissatisfaction.

That same friend that I mentioned above is heterosexual, but checks out women's bodies at the beach on a regular basis. One time, I vividly remember her commenting on a woman wearing a bikini with a belly button piercing, saying how she had balls to wear that. Was she a big girl? Yes. My response to my friend, "Well, how do you know if perhaps she lost weight and her goal for this summer was to wear a bikini and pierce her belly button? Plus, more importantly, good for her to have enough self-esteem and self-worth to be able to pull that off, smile, and be proud of herself."

Looking through my eyes, I want to remind you to look at the bodies on the beach you are attracted to. For example, if you are heterosexual, look at the opposite sex, not the same. I have a newsflash for you, there will always be someone who has something better or worse than you. As far as the woman in the bikini my friend was commenting about, she has something, which happens to be sexier than a size 0 that many of my patients need to strive for. It is called confidence.

My message: embrace your body. Make peace with your body. Be grateful for what it offers you that you forget about. Your legs that can move you from point A to point B, your arms that can freely wrap themselves around the people you love, your stomach that can digest and absorb the nutrients necessary to contribute to your health and well-being, and your ass that provides cushion to you when sitting on a metal chair. I dare you to give it a try! This trait is not shallow. In an unforgiving world, when it comes to yourself and body image, be more forgiving. Once you get there, believe me, you will never turn back, and your mind will be a less busy place!

Enjoy this season, folks. We have been waiting months for it to get here, and truth be told, it will be gone before we know it.

Your Struggle Is Real

Deb-ism #12

You Don't Look Like You Have
An Eating Disorder =
Nine Most Ignorant Words.

FIRST DAY OF SCHOOL GONE WRONG

And here we are. For most, the first day of school is back to reality. It's the beginning of early to bed, early to rise kind of days. School, work, pool closings, thoughts of having to blow out our sprinklers, and even what costume to wear for Halloween (Note: If you haven't noticed, they are already clearing out back to school stuff and replacing it with Halloween candy and costumes, and it's only September 2nd).

Well, with our usual routines returning along with our children rising and having to move along to make the bus so we can move along as well, comes a problem with eating balanced meals. For the last month, my office has been helping my college and high school patients try to figure out where to fit the three standard meals into their extremely busy days necessary for health and wellbeing, even without formal lunch periods.

You see, for most people, with any kind of change begins a push back in many other daily routines. Yes, I agree that change is difficult; but as a firm believer, as well as someone who has personally gone through many life changes and come out better on the other side I can tell you the outcome is worth the effort.

Whether you forgot to pack lunch the night before and didn't have time in the morning because your five-year-old was up all night worrying about his seat on the bus or after cleaning the kitchen last night, you remembered you had to finalize that presentation to your boss tomorrow and needed to review it.

Or, if you packed your kids lunch the night before, why didn't you pack yours? Better yet, why didn't you have your kids pack their own lunch and yours while you were loading the dishwasher after dinner. Win- win. It would have taught them independence as well as provided you with a more nutritious and cost-effective choice for the next day.

Let's face it: Life happens.

I teach my patients on a regular basis, especially this time of year, the value of balanced eating. Your job is to provide those meals three times a day to you and your children and to know how important it is. Food is fuel, energy for your brain to get those things done that are so important every day!

By not providing them, you are setting a poor example to your children as well as getting your new routine off to a poor start.

A granola bar or cup of coffee is not enough to keep the brain working, especially for children who really need nutrients for growth, not just for health and well-being. Side note: not having a lunch period at school is not helping the situation.

With this said, make the time to plan and eat three balanced meals. Somehow, you make the time to brush your teeth and shower daily. Your family and coworkers will thank you just as much when you can stay focused and are not grouchy from not having those meals!

Now that I pointed out the value of making time to pack lunch, let us look at one scenario:

A large population of the patients I treat are teenagers and adolescents. For those of you who do not have children in this age category, I will tell you as a mom and a clinician that this population is the most influenced by their peers and social media. For them, the first day of school, especially if they are going to a new school, is as important as a wedding to adults. They plan their outfits by scouring social media to see the latest and greatest. Get their hair cut. If it is a girl beginning high school, she may even get a manicure and/or a pedicure.

Food to them is the least most important thing on their minds for this important day. Think about it for a moment, you do the exact same things when attending an affair, and just like with them when it is over, a week, a month, or a year later they will be distant memories with only a photo or two left behind that they hold dear.

So, you help them by supplying transportation and money in preparation of their big day. Perhaps take a photo or two and off they go.

They arrive at the first period with their brand-new outfit and shoes, haircuts, and mani/pedis with confidence. And that is when, as the old saying goes, the wheels fall off.

Many of the kids arrived early and were standing around "Julia." Wow, you look amazing! How much weight did you lose? How did you do it?

Your child is watching all of their peers surround and fuss over Julia, and in less than one minute, the value of the new outfit you bought for them and their confidence is gone.

They spend the entire first period glancing over to Julia. This little voice inside their heads tells them how gross they are. Why couldn't you be the thinnest? Why couldn't everyone pay attention to you? You could not hear from your chair how much weight she lost, but you can do it better!

The bell rings to change class. Your child, from losing focus during the lesson, did not hear a word the teacher said, and on the way out the door of the classroom, she opens her backpack and throws her lunch into the garbage. And the first day of school and lack of self-esteem begins.

This exact scenario happens on a regular basis in my office and, believe me, it is happening to your kids, and you do not even know it.

Your Struggle Is Real

"I've never had an eating disorder. I used to get a lot of criticism for how thin I was, and I didn't have a lot of confidence because of it. But I was naturally thin. I always thought it was irresponsible of the media to portray me as someone with an eating disorder because if some girls look up to me, it's a horrifying concept. I listened to the criticism a little too much—and this was pre-social media. It's even crazier to think what women have to deal with now.

—Ellen Pompeo
on How I'm aging in Hollywood
published in People magazine 8/8/16.

***Ellen Pompeo** has teamed with the beauty brand Philosophy on a campaign aimed at dispelling stereotypes about women and aging.*

HOLIDAY SEASON

Now, the holiday season begins: Thanksgiving, Black Friday, Small Store Saturday, Cyber Monday. It's a whirlwind for sure!

The truth of the matter is the holiday season starts in September for my fellow Jewish people with Rosh Hashanah (the Jewish New Year) and the traditional honey and wonderful desserts. Or, for many, Halloween begins the why bother mentality. Candy. In every store and on every end cap. It even appears to be on sale. Next, there's the promise of saving money with the "must buy two" statement. Did you look closely? Really close? How much are you saving? Really saving? Is it worth the $0.40 savings to take it home in the beginning of October after they cleared the back-to-school stuff off the shelves? Remember, Halloween is always on October 31. How will it feel having those bags of candy in your closet for a month? What happens if a family member decides to open one? Hmmmm, you will likely need to buy more, and the "buy two" cycle begins again.

Why bother to eat well? It is the holidays. No time to exercise. Too many parties, too many yummy traditional holiday foods that will not be around again until next year, and too many reasons to make excuses.

Well, guess what folks. You cannot turn off your diabetes, your high blood pressure, your heart disease, or your high cholesterol for the holidays. It is not about clean or organic eating one day and unhealthy eating the next. Look around you. Being mindful of what you're eating is obviously not working. We as a nation are the fattest, most unhealthy in the world.

This message is not just sent from family and coworkers. It is also sent from the media. You will not see a commercial for a weight loss program or gym membership until New Year's Eve. Smart on the food industry and packaging companies, isn't it? They would never waste their advertising dollars on the American on and off mantra this time of year. Be proud of your arduous work and effort, for you are not conforming to this on and off society.

With the holidays, for many people and my patients, also comes an increase in anxiety. Not surprising when you put social situations and an increase in food together.

Believe it or not, for most of my patients, the harder of the two is the first one I wrote: *the social piece.* Seeing family and friends they haven't seen for months or perhaps a full year puts them on heightened awareness. What did I look like last time I saw____? Was I a size 10? What was my weight? What did_____ look like? What did____ eat? Wait a minute; did they even eat?

Keep it simple. Breathe. Live in the moment. Listen to what is being said. Do not blow anything out of proportion. Yeah, yeah, easier said than done, but if you try it, you may enjoy those moments!

So, what is my message? I teach balance. I teach moderation. I teach variety. Most importantly, I teach flexibility. I teach my patients how to make all foods fit. Once you get on board with the right mindset, you reap the benefits each day, even during the holiday season.

On a side note to give a giggle, remember what I said above, that you won't see commercials for diet plans or gym memberships until New Year's Eve? Believe me, those people that show up at the gym the Monday after New Year's will be gone by Valentine's Day. They will be too busy eating chocolate to make it to the gym!!

Your Struggle Is Real

Deb-ism #13

The difference between losers and winners is that losers live in the past and feel sorry for themselves. Winners learn from the past, have lots of persistence, and move on.

SIX STAGES OF CHANGE

Pre-contemplation: You don't even know something needs to be changed. People in your life begin to draw attention to a problem or behavior you have.

Contemplation: You see a habit that needs to be changed, but still aren't ready to act on it.

Preparation: You plan to take action

Action: You actually make the change.

Maintenance: With success, you continue to move forward, despite occasional slip ups. You will try to avoid high risk situations and plan strategies to avoid relapse.

Termination: You did it! Your former problem or addiction will not pose any temptation for you to use ever again, and most importantly, you can cope without fear of relapse.

Your Struggle Is Real

GUYS STRUGGLE TOO

As of this printing, one third of the population of people over their lifetime diagnosed with an eating disorder will be guys. The biggest problem, to me, is because of the stigma girls have issues with food and dieting, most guys do not seek treatment.

Men actually represent the following percentage of those affected with an eating disorder (NEDA):
- 25% anorexia nervosa
- 36% binge eating disorder
- 25% bulimia nervosa

Gay men (about 5% of the male population) make up 42% of men with eating disorders. Men are also more likely to die from anorexia nervosa because it is so often undiagnosed (NEDA).

As mentioned, most often those guys will have BDD and other concurrent disorders mentioned in this book. Muscle dysmorphia, a subtype of body dysmorphic disorder, is quite common with guys as the pressure from society to be muscular becomes the norm. I would say, the things to look for that would point in the direction of a potential problem include spending many hours in the gym, taking supplements (often recommended by a gym rat - not a professional), abnormal eating patterns, or use of steroids. Men and boys who are diagnosed with anorexia are at risk for low levels of Vitamin D and testosterone and are, therefore, at elevated risk for osteoporosis and osteopenia.

As my recovered patient, Ethan Eisenberg, has stated, "I want people to understand the cultural pressures that gay men face in their own community every day with the understanding that so few men are diagnosed with eating disorders. My goal is to illuminate how and why many men get them, from my own experience, so more men or boys can understand that they actually have them. This illness is no joke and the farther away I get from being acutely ill in 2017, the scarier it is that this disease came so close to ending my life. Anorexia Nervosa has the highest mortality rate of any mental illness. I am constantly shocked by how many people struggle."

Your Struggle Is Real

* See Ethan's personal relational story in this book.

Deb-ism #14

Your Body Is The Least Interesting Thing About You.

LETS NOT FORGET:

BODY DYSMORPHIC DISORDER (BDD):

This condition is defined by a preoccupation with what someone sees (extremely common in my male patients) that is either minor or nonexistent. Many who suffer seek plastic surgery or dermatology appointments to "fix" their imperfections. Most people who suffer have a tough time being in public, are perfectionistic, and are preoccupied by the mirror. BDD most often causes those that suffer significant emotional distress and difficulties with day to day functioning. The most common age of onset is 13. Thoughts of suicide and behaviors are quite common.

ORTHOREXIA:

The defining feature of this newer eating disorder is an obsession with eating healthy food and avoiding unhealthy food. What matters most is feeling pure or eating "clean." It often begins where an individual cuts out carbs, gluten, or dairy from their diet. Food needs to be organic, raw, fresh, GMO-free, or you feel a negative emotion attached to whatever you are eating. With this negativity and pure eating often comes nutrition deficiencies that negatively affect your mental and physical well being.

Some warning signs to look out for:
— Compulsive ingredient checking, rigid "good" vs. "bad" food categories which lead to "food rules"

— Obsession with avoiding foods that contain animal products, sugar, salt, fat, or additives
— An obsessive food selection which may result in food choices with less than ten ingredients
— An increased amount of time spent thinking about food
— Avoidance of food prepared or brought by others
— Extreme feelings of guilt when consuming what they label as "unhealthy" foods
— Feeling elated from eating "healthy" while losing interest in other activities they once enjoyed
— Excessive interest in "wellness" lifestyle influencer content
— Noticeable avoidance of foods they used to love because it doesn't appear to be "healthy" anymore.

The tricky thing about this new diagnosis is that it often first appears as a good thing. To an untrained eye, most living with orthorexia can be labeled as "healthy" or "health conscious". Aren't we supposed to eat organic and healthy? When you've allowed it to control every aspect of your life to the point where you aren't going to dinner at your mother-in-laws house because she uses canned vegetables and jarred sauce, or you can't join your friends for dinner at a restaurant because they don't proclaim to have organic chicken, you know you're headed in the wrong direction.

ARFID (Avoidant Restrictive Food Intake Disorder):

Most diagnosed with this eating disorder were called picky eaters. Some had food phobias which were so severe such as a fear of choking or vomiting on a certain food, so they would rather avoid it. Those affected usually are accompanied by severe texture restrictions, or they avoid specific colors, tastes or smells of foods as well. Some will have at least one of the following:

— An eating or feeding disturbance secondary to lack of interest or concern about the adverse effect of eating a certain food
— Weight loss or failure to grow in height or weight
— Nutritional and/or energy deficiencies
— Supplemental dependency or dependence on internal feedings
— Significant interference with psychosocial functioning

Research has been ongoing, but there are a lot of innovative results that prove this condition is not about being a picky eater. I have worked with many children from ages eight and up. The thing that is happening often is, I have teenage patients 15-17 years of age who were passed by as being picky eaters and they so desperately want to be normal eaters. They would love to go out for pizza with their friends, go to the Mall and have lunch in the food court, not have their entire family feel alienated when they go out to eat at restaurants or holiday gatherings without drawing attention to themselves or even worse, not attend at all. After working through the addition of once restrictive foods, many of my patients feel relief as they can go out and fit in. Many of my patients, once diagnosed, also seek added guidance from feeding programs specifically aimed at helping them through these issues.

ED-DMT1 (EATING DISORDERS IN TYPE I DIABETES)
OR USED TO BE CALLED DIABULIMIA:

Many of my eating disorder patients who are insulin dependent or are diagnosed as type I diabetics have developed diabulimia at some point of their journeys. Controlling or manipulating their levels of insulin before or after binging, they think they can manipulate their weight by going into ketosis. These patients will deliberately underuse insulin for the sole purpose of controlling their weight.

The outcome of this very dark manipulation can lead to serious, long - term conditions, including visual disturbances (blurred vision - which can impair driving), kidney, nerve, and circulation damage (neuropathy), heart related conditions, and abdominal pain.

Your Struggle Is Real

Deb-ism #15

Sometimes you need to feel
uncomfortable
until uncomfortable becomes
comfortable.

TESTIMONIALS

The following is a series of essays
from patients and colleagues about their experiences...

From M.B.
*One of my recovered anorexic patients
after three residential treatment centers.*

Lying in a lumpy hospital bed, the distant beeping of a heart monitor and the lurking threat of death interrupted the mundane sterilization of the bleak pediatric ward. As fluids pulsed through the nasogastric feeding tube that was keeping me alive, I felt isolated in the depths of self-pity. I blamed myself for the grave situation I was in, yet simultaneously I wondered if my life had always been destined for tragedy.

At the innocent age of fourteen, I became the skeletal remains of the vibrant, carefree child I once was. The happy stability of my childhood was violently ruptured by my failing health and degrading quality of life. Tragedy became my reality when the words "anorexia nervosa" echoed from the doctor's mouth, and my mother's cry was the only noise that pierced the dreadful silence created by my diagnosis. Terrified of losing the child that was already gone, my parents rushed me to the hospital where I remained for two months. In spite of my suffering, I had difficulty letting go of my paralyzing illness.

Allowing myself to be vulnerable was a great challenge. I refused to relive the past hardships that terrorized me from the untouchable depths of my psyche. Eventually, with extensive time and determination, I slowly began to accept the aspects of my life that I had always forced myself to forget. I came to realize that my childhood wasn't happy as much as it was comfortable- I rarely engaged in activities that interested me if they strayed too far from normalcy. I was swaddled by the privileges of my middle-class town and often turned a blind eye to the needs and struggles of others. I became numb to my father's alcoholism because it destroyed me to see someone I cared so much about deteriorate right in front of me. So I pretended. I pretended that my life was perfect and controlled every aspect of it that I could until it nearly killed me.

There is no particular moment in my battle with anorexia that inspired my liberation. Instead, it was through countless months of therapy and self-reflection that I finally grasped the significance of self-love. I refused to continue living in a reality that was sculpted by those around me. From the fiery, impassioned hues of the autumn foliage to the soft twinkle of the moon and the stars on a cloudless summer night, my lust for life was rekindled. Empowered by all that life has to offer, I became determined to take advantage of everything that I could.

Defining my own path has been harsh and confusing, but it is significantly more fulfilling. I finally have the respect for myself to do what makes me happy, regardless of how others may perceive me. I am far from perfect, and I still have much to learn, but I can confidently say that I am a better person than I was four years ago, and I am constantly improving upon who I was yesterday.

Exposure to the blatant horrors of mental illness has been my gravest struggle, but the immeasurable strength that was needed to overcome it is my sincerest accomplishment. Moving from the canyons of vulnerability and helplessness that allowed me to soar far beyond the highest mountaintops. Most importantly, I learned that adversity and hardship do not constitute a story of tragedy. Instead, they radiate as gospels of limitless hope.

From Emily S.
*This composition is from one of my recovered anorexic
patients who struggled with anxiety.*

As a high school girl who always felt the pressure to fit in and to be perfect, I felt I had no control in my life. That is when I decided to turn to the one thing I felt that I could control: my food. As I withered away, I could no longer recognize myself, nor could my family. I hated the reflection in the mirror as I never thought I was skinny enough or good enough. I became a miserable and toxic person, so fixated on calories and how I was going to throw out my food for the day so I did not have to eat. I lost cheerleading, the one constant in my life, as I could no longer stand without feeling like I would fall over.

My true wake-up call was realizing how my actions were affecting everyone around me and how I was about to lose everything over an obsession I created in my head. Treatment saved my life. Admitting I needed help saved me. If it was not for people like Deb, I would still be in this vicious cycle of not feeling like enough. Today, I love myself. I love the way I look. I eat what I want, and I no longer define myself by my ED. I used to be Emily the anorexic. Today I am just Emily, and that is good enough.

From Sandy Schlessinger, LCSW-R

The disordered relationship I have with food and my body has been with me as far back as I can remember. Numbers, whether it be calories or the scale, have ruled my life, my moods and infiltrated other countless areas of my life. Through this struggle, I found a way (I thought!) of controlling things beyond my control. If I was having a bad day, I would either restrict (no skinny person has a bad day, right?) or binge (for momentary, and I stress momentary, comfort). But these attempts at control became their own beast and ended up controlling me.

I'd feel guilty after binging, irritable and tired after restricting, and the cycle continued for years. Being surrounded by a chaotic life, which I learned we all have, my control no longer worked. It didn't solve any problems and only served to create more. I was hiding food wrappers after overeating, spending way too much time looking in the mirror, comparing myself (inaccurately) to everyone around me, and counting and measuring.

Looking back on the time it took away from the true meaning of life hits me hard. How much time was wasted. Is it still like that? No. Does it come up sometimes? Yes, but I'm aware. I can now eat and not count, I can go months without knowing my weight. I can go up or down a size and not freak out. I can, I can, I can.

That is because of my supports. I got into therapy, am working with a wonderful registered dietitian, am on medications, and my life is happy. I am happy to be in my skin and experience life on life's turns, without the extra bullshit, without the self-sabotage.

I would've never thought it was possible to be where I'm at today, and I guess I'm saying that because I read about it, heard about it from others, and didn't believe it. Whoever is reading this probably feels that doubt too, but it is possible. You can escape the beast, and you are more than a number. You are your personality, your contributions to society, you are a friend, a mother or father, a daughter or son, a neighbor, a partner, an employee or boss. You are all of those things, which are a hell of a lot more important than the size of your pants, which reminds me of this quote by Pema Chodron:

> *"Life is glorious, but life is also wretched. It is both. Appreciating the gloriousness inspires us, encourages us, cheers us up, gives us a bigger perspective, energizes us. We feel connected. But if that's all that's happening, we get arrogant and start to look down on others. There is a sense of making ourselves a big deal and being really serious about it, wanting it to be like that forever. The gloriousness becomes tinged by craving and addiction. On the other hand, wretchedness~ life's painful aspect~ softens us up considerably. Knowing pain is a very important ingredient of being there for another person. When you are feeling a lot of grief, you can look right into somebody's eyes because you feel like you haven't got anything to lose~ you're just there. The wretchedness humbles us and softens us, but if we were only wretched, we would all just go down the tubes. We'd be so depressed, discouraged,*

and hopeless that we wouldn't have enough energy to eat an apple. Gloriousness and wretchedness need each other. One inspires us; the other softens us. They go together."

In a separate card to me:
Thank you so much for all your guidance and support throughout the years. Your gentle and humorous approach is amazing, and it's great knowing you are there to help me through this process.

From E.D.
One of my recovered orthorexic patients who moved out of state with her boyfriend and will pursue law school.

"Recovery is worth it" was a quote I came across a lot while I was recovering from my eating disorder. I honestly didn't believe it at the time, I was much more comfortable in my toxic bubble where I was afraid of any food that wasn't kale, and I was constantly exercising.

I was a high school girl who was a competitive dancer, so I never stopped looking in the mirror and criticizing myself. Top that with the fact that I had a type A personality, plus a mom who was a personal trainer and immersed in the fitness industry, and you get a recipe for orthorexia.

Food, weight, and body image were all I thought about, and I was scared to eat anything that wasn't "clean." I was malnourished and not thinking clearly, but never felt like I was that sick. I became the shell of a person I now know I could be, and I have my amazing nutritionist and therapist to thank for that.

Recovery sucks. It was the hardest thing I ever had to do, and it was not pretty. I forced myself to face my fear of "unclean" foods, dealt with some wicked GERD, and had to look deeper into my anxiety and perfectionistic personality. Nearly seven years after my first appointment with Deb, I can hardly believe that girl was me.

I can now confidently say that recovery is totally and utterly worth it; however, I know what it takes to get there. Learning how to manage that eating disorder voice in the back of your head and put it into its place was a constant battle. It's a winding, bumpy road that doesn't seem like it will end, and although the thoughts may never fully go away, one day you realize that you aren't thinking about food, weight, and body image, and that eating disorder voice inside your head doesn't say much anymore. It's a liberating feeling, and while it makes me sad for the girl that I was while recovering, I know my journey has made me stronger and has shaped me into who I am today. Even though recovery is not at all perfect, I assure you, it is worth it.

From Alyssa B.
NEDA Written by one of my recovered patients
(published in summer 2012):

Pursuit of the Impossible: Perfection.

I remember the exact day it happened. It was a simple thought that turned into an action which ultimately changed my whole life. At fifteen I sought perfection in everything I did, including my sport. I was a competitive, level nine gymnast struggling to fulfill the incredible demands that gymnasts face every day. Between the ages of fourteen and fifteen, I began to work harder than I ever did at anything. To push myself to limits I never thought I could reach. As a result, I became very good at the sport, but, of course, with more skill came more pressure.

I remember the exact thought that came to my mind when I was fifteen. What else can I do to make myself a better gymnast? My answer was that I would become thinner. I believed the thinner I was, the higher I would be able to fly and move through the air. So, I stopped eating. The first few days, I felt deceptively fine. I thought that this was such a great idea and wondered to myself why I didn't think about this before. Then, around the fourth day, I found myself exhausted at practice unable to complete the skills I was required to. I didn't know what to do. I felt so lost, and I didn't want to tell anyone because this was my secret. I also didn't see this as a problem, asking myself, "I'm doing it for the sake of my gymnastics, right?"

Eventually, someone who I know cared a lot about me. I was very hesitant in telling her, but she finally got it out of me and forced me to tell my coach. At this point, I was so early in the disorder that I had not yet started lying to hide it, and I couldn't think of a good enough excuse as to why I was exhausted and unable to do anything at practice. My coach told me we were going to have a talk after practice and to just hang tight for the time being. I didn't know this at the time, but reflecting back on it, I think initially talking with my coach greatly decreased the duration of my eating disorder in the long run.

At first, I listened to her and went home and ate dinner, but soon enough, I was back to restricting. I spent endless nights looking up diet plans and looking up very dangerous "thinspiration" websites and videos. It was then that my eating disorder began to take over my life- obsessing over calories, being consumed by irrational thoughts, and practicing constantly, even when I was dizzy and not feeling well. The irrational thoughts even led me to shave my legs every day because the idea that even .1 inches of hair might add to my weight and make gymnastics that much harder terrified me.

In my eating disorder, I kept pushing and pushing myself to the point that I didn't even know who I was. Eventually, my body couldn't handle not eating, and I often found myself binging. The binging would then lead to purging, frequently in the form of over-exercise. The need to exercise was not about health, and the extent of my exercising only contributed to destroying my health.

In retrospect, it blows my mind that I felt I had to exercise so excessively in order to exceed in a sport that required the impossible: Perfection. I lived with this painful cycle for years. Binging. Exercising. Restricting. Repeat. The eating disorder was controlling my life. I started reading all the books on eating disorders that I could find and saw all of the movies. It was like I was looking for something I couldn't find.

Now, I know that what I was looking for was help that would eventually lead me to my recovery. It wasn't an easy or short road, but today I can proudly say that I do eat normally and no longer feel the pressure to be a specific weight. This took years, and I credit a lot of my success to the help I received from an amazing nutritionist. I also could not have done it without the support of my friends and family. I had a teammate that cared so much about me that she would ask me every day how I was doing and would constantly listen to me. She was there for me when I needed her the most and to this day, I don't know what I would've done without her.

I remember sitting in her car one day after attempting to eat dinner, and she looked at me and said, "Maybe someday you will help girls who struggle with exactly what you are facing."

I looked back at her with a look on my face that shouted, "Absolutely not!" But now, four years after recovering and learning so much about eating disorders and myself, I know that this is exactly what I was meant to dedicate my life to. I am currently attending college in hopes of becoming a Registered Dietitian and a Clinical Psychologist, with the ultimate goal of opening a rehabilitation center for the treatment of eating disorders.

You can recover from an eating disorder. It's taking those first few steps and believing in that light at the end of the tunnel that will change your life.

Card from Alyssa to me:
I wanted to thank you for everything you have done for me this summer. You have changed my life in so many ways and were somehow able to get through to me. I never thought I would have a normal relationship with food again, and now I finally do.

From S.D.
*One of my recovered anorexic patients who presently
moved out of state to pursue an incredible career choice
with her boyfriend at the age of 21.*

*The number:
it was more,
but it felt like less.*

*less important
less defining
less controlling*

*I didn't love it,
but I didn't hate it.*

*I didn't want to keep it,
but I didn't want to change it.*

*it was different,
but so was I.*

From Kelsie C.

One of my recovered anorexic patients,
who has a very active Instagram account where she is very open
about her journey and so grateful for where she is now.
This is from a book she self-published called "My Devil Twin."

About 200 years ago, there lived a man by the name of Edward Mordrake. Mordrake was born with a very rare congenital disorder, Diprosopus, which caused another face to sprout from the back of his head. The Mordrake legend shows how his natural face was so alluring that it was almost godly, but the face that was on his back? Hideous! Also, according to this legend, his other face exhibited signs of life and intelligence and even smiled when Mordrake was upset. At night, the face would keep him up with wicked utterances and temptations. Eventually, it drove him mad, and although Mordrake was considered incredibly gifted in all areas of study, he completely isolated himself from society. Many times he tried convincing doctors to remove what he called his "devil twin," but no doctor would dare to attempt it. Mordrake even tried drowning it in the bathtub, but it would never quite work. He saw no way out and committed suicide. He was only 23 years old.

In many ways, Edward Mordrake's life parallels my own. My disorder was my very own devil twin, I constantly followed the relentless "orders" of a voice inside my head. For a long time, it made me go through crazy measures in order to please it. I was so preoccupied with my devil twin that I never realized how long I had actually been mad. Living with and fighting an eating disorder can be so tricky and complex that it's damn near impossible to describe to someone without either living through one, or living with someone who has.

There's never one specific trigger for an eating disorder; rather, it's a multitude of things that slowly build up until it becomes a deadly parasite. Unfortunately, those of us with an eating disorder become expert at seeming like we have it together. We camouflage our devil twin by excelling at school, work, and other activities. No one would ever know it's there, but for us. It gives us its wicked utterances so often that we eventually can longer differentiate whose voice is whose.

Like Mordrake, no matter how many times we try to drown our twin, it never goes away, at least not on its own. Luckily, recovery is possible- difficult, yes, but possible. Suicide is NOT the only way out, but I'd be lying if I said I didn't feel suicidal for some time. It took some serious work for me to get comfortable enough to open up about my feelings. I remember my mom emphasizing one's need for "peeling back layers," because then and only then can someone free themselves from their devil twin.

In many ways, an eating disorder is like an addiction. For instance, the first time one engages in an eating disorder behavior, it is often to cope with complicated feelings of depression, loneliness, and/or disgust. Immediately following an episode, it is common to experience an intense euphoria that doesn't last long, but it's only the devil twin's face overpowering our own and masking how we truly feel on the inside. As a result, the person with the eating disorder slowly becomes trapped in a cycle of addiction, craving the feeling the behavior gives us, no matter how long that feeling lasts. Sadly, we do it again and again and yet again until it's completely out of control. In my opinion, any food-related addictions are amongst the hardest to break because of the fact that food is essential to life. Unlike quitting cigarettes where in order to beat the addiction, one must get them out of their life for good, we need food in order to survive. It is difficult (emotionally, mentally, and physically) to learn how to eat in a healthy fashion and quiet our devil twin during meals and snacks. Not to mention that every time we are presented with food, we are confronted with our eating disorder urges that we've associated with for so long.

It's extraordinarily difficult to admit that a problem exists because of how easy it is to normalize our behaviors when having been controlled by our evil twin for so long. It becomes scarier to picture our lives without the eating disorder than it is with it because it has been the only thing there for us so many times. Like Mordrake, it secludes us, taking away all of our opportunities by constantly whispering to us that we aren't worth them, and we believe it. Sometimes, we are so weak from the devil twin that there's no energy left to deal with anything else. It has embedded itself so deep inside our brains that we believe we need it in our life.

Eating Disorders go so much deeper than food. Food is just the object we abuse to deal with our emotions. So I guess that begs the million dollar question, "What exactly is the cause of an eating disorder?" Well, there have been many theories, but at the end of the day, there's no way to pinpoint just one. I can tell you for sure that it's not just a matter of "choosing" to eat too much or too little.

From Victoria L.
*One of my recovered patients who struggled
with bulimia. Presently, she writes a mindfulness blog
to empower others.*

During my time working with Deb, my life changed completely. As a young girl who previously struggled with anxiety, self-confidence, and other challenging life experiences, I developed an eating disorder during college that absolutely took hold of my life and my mind. Deb calls these thoughts the uninvited guests. I came into her office completely lost, and without her, I would never have the life I do today. Her compassion and knowledge for this journey are unparalleled, and every lesson learned in our weekly appointments helped shape the human being I am now.

Recovery is a difficult road, but it is most certainly one worth taking. In fact, I've turned my past into motivation to help fellow young women prioritize self-care and mindfulness by starting a blog, and in May 2021 I graduated from university with a close to perfect GPA. None of this would be possible without Deb, her wisdom, and her passion for what she does.

From Ethan E.
One of my recovered patients.

For much of my life (going back into childhood), I have struggled with food and body image issues. With a formal diagnosis of anorexia nervosa occurring at age fifteen, it may seem ironic that, in my younger years, I actually struggled with overeating. The same held true with exercise; by the age of fifteen, I was compulsively or overexercising; but up until the age of twelve, I resented any form of physical activity.

When I first met Debra, she taught me that it isn't actually ironic at all. It is very common for people with eating disorders to struggle at both extremes (over and undereating/overexercising) at different points within their lives. It was imperative that she explained this to me, considering I incorrectly learned in treatment that anorexics rarely struggle with overeating before or after starting recovery. However, when I originally saw Debra, after many months of program treatment for anorexia, I began facing binge eating again.

She helped me understand that there was more work to be done (mentally) if I was still experiencing extreme behaviors with food. She encouraged me to do that work under the guidance of my therapist with whom she worked closely. She taught me that physiologically, I could aid this process of recovery through eating regularly, eating foods I enjoy (she calls it "all foods fit"), and eating enough.

Fast forward to four years after I first worked with Debra. It was a few months ago that I decided to see Debra again even though I consider myself in full remission from my eating disorders. I work as a personal trainer, teaching multiple, high intensity classes within the week (such as Cycle and HIIT). I was finding it hard enough to eat food to sustain myself, especially being a busy college student with a full course load as well. I found myself losing small amounts of weight, not because I had a compulsive desire to like I did in my anorexia, but because I didn't actually know how much food to eat with such an active lifestyle.

Remember, I was an incredibly inactive child that didn't play sports, so I never learned along with my more active peers how to intuitively eat to support my activity. Debra re-educated me on my nutrition in a way that was similar, yet different from my eating disorder treatment. The compassion, crystal clear advice and knowledge, and a touch of snarky wit all remained the same. What changed was that she empowered me in so much of what I already knew from my recovery. I just needed to take it to the next level. This made my adjustment to my more active lifestyle so effortless and empowering.

Today, I am recovered from my eating disorders and maintaining a robust, healthy weight as a personal trainer and so much of that is thanks to Debra.

Written by Carolyn G. Psych NP

It is very difficult for me, a mother with an eating disorder, to help my girls with food issues; they have never been much of an issue. My nineteen year old daughter has gained ten pounds during Covid so far. She was shocked about the weight gain and didn't know how it happened.

My daughter had come to me twice to talk. We spoke about the fact that she works in a physical fitness environment and before the pandemic had gone to the gym a couple of times per week. Recently, she hadn't, but her eating had not changed. We talked about how she sits and eats candy in bed while watching TV without a thought. How she ate heartily late at night and sometimes did not eat all day. She cried. She told me that she loved her body and does not feel fat, but her clothes were tight, and she was genuinely confused.

At each point when she asked me direct questions, I realized how few skills I had to help her. I shared with her that I knew an expert (you) who could help her. She welled up with tears at the thought of talking with someone about food because she was afraid she would be told not to eat or wouldn't be able to eat the things she loved. I told her that you were not like that at all. I shared with her what we discussed at our first meeting because I wanted her to see that she could eat anything and you would be able to help her have success. I told her that she did not have great pathology to seek guidance for wellness self-care.

I have advised her that I do not want to give her a bias on how to frame her relationship with food or to change her relationship with food because of my own struggles. I told her she has her own path as well as wonderful resources. I told her that one of my greatest fears was passing on my eating disorder to the next generation, so she would be best helped by a professional, and I would always be there to provide love and support. Issues of food, fat, the fit of clothing, self-image, and anxiety are a holy ground with a nineteen-year-old girl. My daughter seemed vulnerable.

This big conversation lasted two hours last night, and she thanked me (something she rarely does). I think it will take time for her to process the information.

Deb, you have changed my life. My weight is still high, but I don't have the shame, disgust, and hatred I had for myself when I came through your door. That is huge. I am still hard on myself; but I am much kinder in comparison to the past. I am able to work and feel I have something to give, and that is because of you. I have had many years of experience trying to help people with their health. I know now that so much of that time was spent giving to people all of the things that I could never have given to myself. At times, I have found it overwhelming as to how damaged I had become, but instead of staring at the damage, I am able to feel joy at how much better I have become.

My journey will never end, but I see the promised land. I can now help people with a full heart because I am willing to experience the healing of my own wounds. That is from you. I have hope for everyone I help because I know that if I can get better, anyone can. I know you are aware of how far I have come. I know the mark of your success is not about weight loss. For me, it was never about weight. It was never about food. But it had always come back to the weight and food. However, food and weight are no longer my identity. Food and weight have become demoted to becoming a personal barometer; that is from you.

After listening to my daughter last night, I watched her throw out her two pound bag of mini chocolate bars after she went up to her room and cleaned it out of food that triggered her. I told her she did not have to throw them away. She said, "I know, but I don't need two pounds." She is not ashamed.

When she left, I went to the cabinet and ate two coffee mugs full of peanut butter pretzels. I did not even connect it. When I did connect it, I stopped and went to bed. This morning I have been so emotional, and I feel I can do better for myself. I wish for myself the healing I wish for her. I am such a slow learner. You not only taught me that I deserve better, but you have held my hand until I believed it. I have so much love and gratitude for you and what you have given me.

From Carolyn Hersh, LCSW

Recovery When Grieving by
(posted on 11/15/18 in eatingdisordertherapyla.com)
Carolyn is not only in full recovery, but she is a LCSW for a residential
treatment center in California where she provides a relational feel
in her treatment towards recovery from an eating disorder.

On May 8, 2017, my mother died from complications from cancer. It was an unexpected death. I still can't believe she died. My mom was diagnosed in January and passed away in May. She had gone to the hospital for trouble breathing and never left.

I can clearly remember going back to my childhood home and seeing her sneakers in her room waiting for her to return to them. Never to feel her embrace again, I cried so hard seeing everything she had touched just days before but left. I was one of those things that she left.

It's been more than a year now since I lost my mom. It was a year that tested me in so many ways: emotionally, physically, and spiritually. One thing I had to face was my eating disorder and my longstanding recovery would play out through the worst thing that has ever happened to me.

I have my own history of emotional eating and bulimia nervosa. It started at a young age. Whenever I was sad as a child, my mom's solution to cheer me up was a trip to the bakery for a giant cookie. My emotional eating and my hatred of being the larger kid was just one of the many factors that led me to a path of destructive behaviors of binging, purging, and restricting.

I've been through enough therapy and treatment that I am able to recognize moments when I find myself starting to eat mindlessly. I check in with what emotions or events are going on. I had, for the most part, overcome being an emotional eater, but then, I was hit with an intensity of emotions that I had never felt before. The seven stages of grief are very real, and I definitely went through and felt each of them.

My anger, my sadness, my pleading to bring my mom back, to having brief moments of acceptance washed over me on a daily basis. My sadness felt like someone placed a brick on top of my heart. Trying to breathe became difficult at times. I was angry, intensely angry, at cancer, the doctors, the hospital, at G-d, at my mother, and at myself. We hear so often how eating disorders fester when we feel a loss of control. Losing my mother was the ultimate reminder, "You have absolutely no control over this."

In the early weeks and even months of living in a world where my mother no longer existed, I wanted comfort and distraction. I wanted food. I wanted alcohol. I wanted anything that would take this pain away. In those moments of pure sadness, I consumed. I knew full well this wasn't the way to handle my emotions. I decided I needed to reach out to my dietitian because yes, even professionals need tune-ups. I remember sitting in my dietitian's office crying because I had gained weight and was feeling out of control with my body and my feelings. I quickly felt hypocritical as an advocate for all bodies being beautiful and guilty because weight gain should not be something I should be crying about.

I had lost my mother. Worse things had occurred rather than gaining a few pounds. My dietitian reminded me that I knew how to eat and that my body would go back to where it should be when I honored my hunger and satiety cues. But, then she shocked me by saying, "Carolyn, maybe you needed to allow yourself to binge in those moments. So it happened. You binged. It's done. Now, go back to your real coping skills."

My dietitian gave me permission to accept my binges. She demonstrated compassion for me when I had no self-compassion. She was right. Sometimes, we have to be okay with where we are. My dietitian did not give me the green light to revert back to maladaptive behaviors. She pushed me back on a path of not beating myself up during a time when the last thing I needed was to hurt myself more.

So how do you manage recovery in a time of grief?

Don't go back to your eating disorder. Just don't. You know it won't help and when you are feeling low, why make yourself feel lower? But, if you skip a meal or eat a few extra cookies just know that it is not a relapse. I did not consider my binging moments a relapse. They happened. I engaged, and then I stepped away. Be gentle toward yourself and give yourself permission to say, "It's okay it happened. Now, what can I do to get back to my recovery?" Go back to your coping skills. Maybe I could have engaged in binging and purging. Maybe I could have thrown my hands in the air and said, "What's the point?" But I didn't. In all honesty, I knew this wasn't something I wanted. So, I made a list of things for me to do to help me through those really tough moments. I took time off from work and went figure skating with friends. The ice was always a very therapeutic place for me, and just being able to feel that cold air whip across my face made me feel happy.

I spent time journaling, cuddling with my dog, and reaching out to friends and family when I needed to talk. I began nightly walks with one of my girlfriends during which we had heart to hearts. I made self- care a priority. You have to. The small lapses that I fell into never once trumped the real self-care that I was doing for myself. If I had beaten myself up for binges and weight gain then it could have sent me on that spiral to a full relapse. Self- care may mean forgiving yourself for your lapses. Forgiving myself helped me continue to move forward.

Death really sucks. Losing someone you love is painful. It can be a torturous pain. There is no way around that. Losing my mother and thinking about her still to this very moment makes my stomach twist, my heart pound, and my eyes water. There will be bad days. I use a lot of radical acceptance in my grief where I acknowledge this is how it is and I have to figure out now how I continue to live in a world where my mom isn't calling me. It's hard to do. Believe me, there are days I do not want to accept this, but if I have to pull from my DBT workbook, acting the opposite is what gets me through the rough days. I don't want to accept that my mother is gone, but that is the reality. I do not, however, have to forget her and how she has impacted my life.

It's okay to cry. It's okay to feel whatever it is you are feeling, and it is okay if those feelings come and go in minutes or if they last for days. There is no wrong way to grieve. During my grief I went to Nashville for a vacation, I went out on weekends with friends and laughed, and I eventually moved to California. I manage to feel happy on some holidays and cry on others. I do not stop living, but I allowed for the grief to take space in my life.

In the end, going back to my eating disorder would just have caused more chaos in an already chaotic time in my life. I know it won't give me control, it won't make me happy, and it certainly will not bring my mother back. I have this blue butterfly pendant necklace my mom bought me before I went into an intensive outpatient program. It gave me strength then, and I wear it now to continue to remind myself that my mother was every bit a part of my recovery and is every bit still a part of me. Now, why would I want to throw all of that away?

From Allison

This essay was written by one of my recovered anorexic patients who was previously admitted to a residential treatment facility twice.

Recovering from anorexia was the most difficult task I've had to accomplish in my life. Thinking back to the sad and horrifying memories still leaves me in shock. I remember the depressing days being terrified digesting a morsel of food, and feeling the need to burn every non-existing calorie off. I also remember being trapped in treatment centers on a feeding tube, and the struggle to regain weight.

Recovery always felt unreachable in my eyes, and after four years stuck in a toxic mindset, I was able to turn my life around for the best. I want everyone struggling to know that if you are struggling like I was, that there is hope and you will not feel like this forever. There is way more to your life than an eating disorder, and recovery is more than possible.

From Geena M.
Honest composition from one of my patients
who struggled with binge eating disorder
and restricting to compensate.

For over six months, I starved myself and exercised excessively and dropped an excessive amount of weight. I became addicted to losing weight, even though it was destroying my physical and mental health. I restricted myself so much that when I finally broke and started eating, I ate everything in sight. I would eat until I couldn't breathe and then starve myself the next day. It was a continuous cycle of binge eating and restricting. I started gaining an excessive amount of weight.

When I first came to Debra Spector a little over a year ago, I was hopeless thinking I would never recover from my eating disorder. From the second I met her to this day, I have learned more about health than I have in my entire life. She not only guided me to the path of recovery, but educated me first to help understand my eating disorder. She didn't just give me a meal plan and expect me to forget about my eating disorder and follow it; she got to know me. This gave her the ability to guide me on a path that was best fitted for me and my personality. She is so passionate about her job and helping people in which she formed a relationship/bond with me. She began to understand me more than anyone could.

I gained thirty-five pounds from binge eating, but now I am back to my original weight. This was huge progress; however, I am not fully recovered as I do have slip ups and binge ever so often. Whenever this happens, I know I have Debra by my side to help me get back on track. I would never be where I am today without her. She is truly an inspiration and role model in every aspect of life.

From R.S.
Written with love
This thank you card was from one of my recovered anorexic patients who,
previous to beginning her journey to recovery with me, was admitted to a
residential treatment center where she was told she needed a G-tube feeding.
When my patient asked what she could do to prevent that she was told she
would need to drink six Ensure Pluses (supplements) daily on top of her meal
plan. She chose the latter option and is completely recovered.

Her card:
Throughout life, you meet all different kinds of people. Some who have a gift for helping others. Some who give wisdom, comfort, and care. Some who tell you which direction to turn and some who will lead you there themselves. Some who warm your heart and some who import you with smiles and laughter. Lucky for me, I met you, a person who possesses all of these qualities.

You have opened my eyes to a world of possibilities. You have honestly made a real difference in my life. You've touched my heart in many ways, and words cannot describe how thankful I am to have you in my life as part of my recovery team. You honestly have a true gift of wisdom, You have shown me to strive for my dreams and accept me for me, along with my flaws and weaknesses. You've shown me that my eating disorder can't tear me down if I take control, that it can only make me stronger.

Thank you for showing me that I must love my body and all the things it does for me and to always keep my head up high. I love you and no amount of words can truly express my gratitude.

Nine years later, I received the following card along with her wedding, pregnancy, and gender reveal party pictures. What I saw was happiness:

As the holiday season is approaching, I sit here and reflect on my life, and how beyond blessed I am. I can think back to a time when I didn't feel this way (or should I say, didn't allow myself to feel this way). Some say it is hard to remember how they felt many years ago, but I can feel it like it was yesterday.

I remember feeling like my life was not worth living; that I would never find true happiness unless the number on the scale read lower each day. That my body was ugly, fat, and unacceptable. However, I am so grateful to now know that I am not just a number on a scale or size "00" jean size. I am a loving daughter, sister, and friend. I am a home-owner, career woman, loving wife (I got married in 2019) and am soon to be a rock star mommy! I am due 1/21!

I never thought this time would be possible for me, that I would be at a place in my life where I don't even think about my weight or the calories I am eating. At a place that as my belly grows and the rest of my body is swelling, I actually enjoy it knowing I am growing another life! And I have you to thank for that.

Thank you for giving me the strength to fight for my life. Thank you for holding me up when I didn't have the strength to hold myself. Thank you for believing in me and never giving up. Thank you for helping me get to a point where I can be thankful to see my belly grow. They are 100% correct that it takes a village, so thank you for being a part of my village and for always instilling positivity into my life.

I know I will take the lessons from you and instill them into my children. I will not instill fear of food into their heads, but joy in knowing a meal will not only give their body energy to live a fulfilling life, but that food will be around our family time at the table, laughing and enjoying. I hope to see you soon and bring my son over to meet you.

From JC ~ Allison's Mom
(previous collection)

"Running on Empty"

There is a song; Running on Empty, by Recording Artist, Jackson Browne. This song has been on my Iphone playlist for many years. Not only do I find it motivational because I am a runner, the lyrics also hit a deeper place. "Gotta do what you can just to keep your love alive, trying not to confuse it with what you do to survive." Translation; live your passion instead of going through the motions. Throughout my life, this song has played a part in nudging me along my G-d given path, helping me navigate the proverbial road. I also relate to the song title in another way, a very literal way. Running on Empty. Going and going. Pushing forward when you feel like there's nothing inside to fuel you both physically and mentally. As a mother to a daughter who suffered anorexia nervosa, we hit a bump in that road when she turned just twelve years old. I had no idea of the journey we were about to begin. I say "we" because I was fortunate not to have my daughter not to travel alone, at least not for long. As she was embarking her preteen years, I was focused on typical coming of age stuff such as: should I buy her a phone? Should I allow her to go to the mall for the first time with a friend? Is she ready to make the transition from the clothing at Justice to the clothing at Hollister? Never would I have thought of the darkness which had begun to take over, right under my eyes without me even seeing it sneak in.

What started out as what I thought were solely gastrointestinal issues, became so much more. There were more signs. Signs I didn't see for what they really were. I didn't realize what my daughter was hiding inside and what breaks my heart is that I couldn't help her from the very beginning, because the possibility of her having an eating disorder never entered my mind. This diagnosis was a new reality which I needed to accept. Not that easy. It's never easy to just "accept" when your child's health is in jeopardy. However, as a close family friend sternly told me, "time is of the essence." What I couldn't see was clearly seen by others. My daughter has always had such a great appetite. She had always been so full of confidence. How could this possibly be happening? I felt so blind, but as my friend clearly implied, I needed to act fast?

As my daughter's illness progressed, I stayed as strong as I could for her on the outside but felt so completely helpless inside. I was sad, worried, confused, angry, and most of the time drained. I was literally running on empty. I felt saddened mostly because I felt she was missing out on her middle school years, (in hindsight, those are rough years anyway), but she still deserved to have them. I wanted "normal" for my daughter instead of being in and out of the physician's offices several times a week. She was missing out on making friendships and not being able to attend school. This was not in our plan. This illness found HER. I did everything I needed to do, listened to every instruction. There is nothing I didn't try. From various surgical procedures, radiology testing, a multitude of blood work and inpatient hospital treatment. The illness still came and it was here to stay for a while. It occupied three years of her life. My daughter had gone outpatient for most of the duration of her eating disorder. My eternal appreciation is devoted to her team of doctors. Weekly visits to Adolescent Medicine, Psychological Therapy and Nutrition sessions were the trifecta crucial to my daughters care and eventual recovery. The weekly nutrition sessions with Debra Spector brought us both out of the darkness and into a new light. We learned about weight and body image in a way where I could understand my daughter better. For the first time, I saw hope. My daughter began to grow and from that growth, she thrived. Everything eventually fell into place. Her grades improved, friendships were made, she went back to gymnastics and she even joined the varsity track team! Most importantly, I began to notice that she was beginning to enjoy food again. It brought back the memory I had of her as a little girl begging me to buy her a McDonalds happy meal and not just for the free toy!

The road to recovery was trying, but with the right nutritional information supplied to us, we were able to work through the tough days together. As time went by, those tough days were few and far between. My daughter has learned how to take car of herself. Now at age sixteen, she prepares some of her own meals, whereas before I had her on a strict schedule of how many calories she needed to intake each day. After so long, it feels liberating for both of us. She has blossomed in every area of life. I look forward to seeing all she's yet to achieve. Now she is running full of energy and enthusiasm.

From TJ

Written with a grateful heart by a mother whose daughter suffered from severe anxiety and was at such a low body weight when I initially treated her. She had to go inpatient for refeeding so the medication she would be put on could actually work. She then was discharged to me and is now in full recovery!

"After in-patient treatment, she will see me." When I heard those words from Debra Spector, the registered dietitian/nutritionist treating our daughter for anorexia, my head started to spin even more out of control. I looked at Deb through what seemed like a long, dark tunnel and said, "Wait, won't she be cured when she returns home from inpatient?" The roller coaster ride became even more daunting.

I've never liked roller coasters, but this one was the one I truly despised. It was truly wicked, out of control, and deadly. It all started (at least when we found out) the day before Halloween, and within a few weeks, our daughter was in medical distress. She hid her weight loss very well. She was a wee one to start, and she was very clever! That was until we met Debra.

There was no getting around her, her expertise, and her knowledge of treating eating disorders. She outsmarted our daughter and amazed us. Her compassion was obvious, and her need to save our daughter's life was her all out priority. We wondered if she had other patients, a family, or a life outside of helping our daughter. It didn't seem like it could be possible. Deb's coaching and techniques about nutritional balance for our daughter, who was nearing death, her meal plans, and the mindset she taught our daughter, let her ease into recovery ~ which, by the way, when she was sick was the last thing our daughter wanted.

Our daughter's recovery is the most important thing she loves about her life today ~ she's healthy and living! Debra worked so hard with our daughter and family, and she truly is the reason our daughter is alive and in recovery from anorexia. Debra is also the reason those we referred to her who were suffering with an eating disorder are in recovery and alive today. They too, were treated by Deb.

It's a must to be treated by someone who really specializes in eating disorders, not just someone who says they work with eating disorders. It's a specialty, and recovery and living depend on it. Remember this name, Debra Spector, if you or someone you know suffers from an eating disorder.

Written by my colleague and friend:
Michele Morganstern, Ph.D

"You don't want to treat eating disorders. Patients with eating disorders never get better." I was a – first-year clinical psychology doctoral student listening to my professor's lecture. I recall thinking, how could people with eating disorders never get better? I was baffled and confused as to why a psychology professor, a mentor, would be so pessimistic regarding the treatment of an entire patient population. I chose to receive specialized training in eating disorders to see for myself. I worked at an inpatient and partial hospital eating disorder program where my responsibilities included arranging discharge care plans. I was disappointed to learn just how few providers there were in the community who would provide care to these patients. It was incredibly disheartening to see them readmitted to the hospital after either working with inexperienced outpatient therapists or after not being able to find one at all.

I have spent the last twelve years as an independent clinical psychologist in private practice. I have dedicated a large portion of my practice to the treatment of eating disorders. It is indeed challenging work, requiring a strong and active therapeutic stance and a team of professionals working together. Eating disorder symptoms don't just disappear after a few sessions. They are complicated and challenging mental health disorders that require both time and expertise to treat.

Eating disorders are generally viewed as separate entities from those who suffer from them. This information is often surprising to my patients, for they are convinced that they and their eating disorders are one and the same. Labeling and visualizing their eating disorders are often helpful treatment tools. One of my youngest patients named her eating disorder Ursula after the villainous sea witch from the movie The Little Mermaid. Of all the metaphors I have heard, it is in fact Ursula and her winding tentacles that best capture the struggle of eating disorder recovery. There are so many facets to these disorders, so many "rules," and so many damaging beliefs. Patients truly feel enveloped by multiple tentacles of irrational thoughts and behaviors, all holding steadfast, all demanding to be followed. After working hard to remove one tentacle, there is often another right there waiting to entangle her even more.

With patience, with perseverance, with support, and with motivation, eating disorders do eventually release themselves and disappear into the sea. It is incredibly gratifying to guide a patient through recovery and watch her slowly be freed, tentacle by tentacle. Imprisoned minds are set free to once again experience and enjoy life. Blank, frightened eyes are replaced with ones that are curious and excited to see what their future holds. It is an honor to work so closely with these patients and comforting to know that I've helped them to define their worth as so much more than a number on a scale.

Sometimes, I think about making a visit to my somewhat ignorant graduate school professor. I would tell him what I do, in fact, I want to treat eating disorders and that my patients do absolutely get better with appropriate treatment. I would tell him with pride that there is nothing else I'd rather devote my career to.

DEBRA SPECTOR, MS, RDN, CDN

Written by Allison H. Eliscu, MD, FAAP
Associate Professor of Clinical Pediatrics
Division Chief of Adolescent Medicine
Stony Brook Children's Hospital

Thoughts About Eating Disorders from an
Adolescent Medicine Physicians Perspective

Stereotypically, many people think eating disorders only occur in teen girls or in wealthy individuals. The truth is that eating disorders do not discriminate. People of any race, gender, socioeconomic status, age, and religion can be affected by these disorders. They are far more prevalent than people think. At least thirty million people in the United States suffer from an eating disorder. Anorexia nervosa, for example, is the third most prevalent chronic disease among youth, after asthma and Type I diabetes. Yet across the board there is frequently an embarrassment that comes along with this diagnosis. Patients are embarrassed to tell friends, family members, or even siblings that they're struggling with an eating disorder. But why? There isn't the same embarrassment when telling people they have mono or diabetes, but there's something about eating disorders (or mental health conditions in general), that embarrasses people. So people suffer and struggle in secret, sometimes too ashamed to seek treatment.

I frequently hear patients struggling with an eating disorder tell me that other people, mom and dad included, "Just don't get it." "They tell me to 'Just eat.' Do they really think it's that easy?" And in some sense, they're right. Most people really don't get it. People who don't have an eating disorder or haven't had a similar experience usually struggle to comprehend it. How can they? For most people, eating seems so natural, something we do every day without thinking about since we were babies. How can it be that hard to just eat?

Here are a few points to help people understand what it's like to live with an eating disorder and some tips that we, as friends, family members, or professionals, can use to help someone reach recovery:

Firstly, and most importantly, remember, it is not as easy as "Just eating." Eating disorders can take over the mind and make each bite agonizingly painful. The eating disorder (or ED) thoughts can become obsessive where teens can't focus on work because they're obsessed thinking about "How many calories have I already consumed today? What will I eat later, and how will I work off those calories so I can lose weight?" Many people with an eating disorder know they have to eat and are aware, on some level, that the ED thoughts are illogical or unhealthy. Unfortunately, when weight loss becomes a sign of discipline and achievement, and weight gain or eating becomes synonymous with failure and loss of control, it really becomes challenging to "Just eat."

The obsessive thoughts can become addictive, dominating the mind and not allowing other thoughts in. One 18-year-old patient struggling with an eating disorder described going to her mother's retirement party. She recalls that she did not hear a single word of the speeches honoring her mother because she was too preoccupied with thoughts about the upcoming meal, the water and rolls already on the table, and what she would allow herself to eat and drink since it was only 11 a.m., and she no longer allowed herself to drink liquids before noon. She was focused on trying to "appear normal," avoid passing out, and avoid embarrassing her mother on her big day.

Some people compare these addictive, obsessive thoughts to a drug addiction. There lies one major difference between these two conditions, recovered drug addicts can live productive lives avoiding their previous drug of choice. In fact, many drug rehab programs encourage addicts to avoid people or places they associate with their drug use. Eating disorder patients do not have these options. They cannot avoid eating. They instead must face their trigger multiple times per day to live.

Secondly, it is important to remember that many people with anorexia have a distorted body image. For example, others may see an individual that is extremely and unhealthily skinny, but the individual looks in the mirror and sees a body that is overweight or fat. Their brain is literally distorting the image that they are seeing. Oftentimes when explaining this phenomenon to parents, I will compare it to a patient I met when I was a medical student during my psychiatry rotation. This young gentleman was diagnosed with schizophrenia and was hospitalized because of increased hallucinations. He sat on his hospital bed and very clearly described to me seeing an angry appearing person on the other side of the room. I looked across the room and only saw an empty chair; there was no one else in the room. I told him that I did not see a person in the chair, and it was probably his mind playing tricks on him. He told me that I could bring 100 doctors into the room to tell him that there was no person in the chair, and he understood that, but when he looked at the chair, he still saw an angry guy sitting there. What could he do? His mind was seeing something that wasn't really there.

Body distortion is similar. You can tell someone over and over that they're not fat or that they're too skinny, but if they see something different when they look in the mirror, it becomes very difficult not to act on that image.

Next, if you think someone you know may have an eating disorder, trust your gut! For many individuals with an eating disorder, the first instinct is to deny that they have a problem or minimize their symptoms. If your sister goes to the bathroom or takes a shower immediately after eating, she may not just be freshening up her makeup; she may be purging. If your son insists on going to the gym twice a day, even on holidays and cannot break strict routines, he may have an eating disorder. Likewise, a friend who only eats "clean" foods, cuts out a lot of food groups, and obsessively follows healthy blogs may have an eating disorder. As a parent, friend, sibling, or professional, you have to trust your gut. Take them to a doctor or a therapist to address your concerns and challenge their denial, even if they tell you that your instincts are wrong.

For many individuals with an eating disorder, the first attempt to get help is a visit to their primary care physician or pediatrician's office. Although your primary doctor may know you and your family quite well, they may not have a lot of experience detecting or managing an eating disorder. I have met many patients who have been falsely reassured by their primary care providers, saying that they are healthy or do not have an eating disorder because their weight is not, yet, in an unhealthy range or their heart rate or blood work is normal. In fact, many patients with eating disorders are at a normal weight or are even overweight. Additionally, having a normal blood work or heart rate does not rule out having an eating disorder since most adolescents or young adults with an eating disorder usually have normal lab values and vital signs. In other words, don't be falsely reassured and, again, trust your instincts.

If your pediatrician isn't listening to you or isn't providing enough support, then seek more specialized help. Find an adolescent medicine specialist or psychiatrist who specializes in this field. Look for a registered dietitian or therapist with expertise in helping individuals with eating disorders.

Lastly, one of the most important things to understand about eating disorders is they almost never get better on their own without some level of treatment. Anorexia or bulimia nervosa is not like the flu or even mono which resolve on their own with time. Those struggling with an eating disorder generally do not just wake up one day and feel better without facing this disorder head on and really challenging and treating it. EDs are also not a phase that someone will outgrow. Residential and inpatient eating disorder units are filled with adults who developed their eating disorder when they were in their teens or early twenties and were never completely treated. Individuals with an eating disorder are at risk for significant medical complications, such as irregular heart rate, kidney problems, bone loss, and decreased immune system (so you can't fight off infections as effectively). We also see changes in the brain function causing depression, anxiety, trouble concentrating, and poor memory.

Please do not let this picture discourage you! You can beat an eating disorder! With the support of close friends, family members, and a specialized multidisciplinary professional team (including a registered dietitian, , therapist, and medical provider), eating disorders can be treated; if you want them to be treated. To make progress you have to challenge those very thoughts that are the most controlling.

One of my seventeen-year-old patients best explained this idea to me. She had been battling anorexia nervosa for three years, and her parents had recently told her that she would not be allowed to go away to college if her symptoms did not improve. She decided, with the help of her treatment team, that she did not want her ED to get in the way of her college aspirations. So, she started to challenge her ED thoughts. She describes how she was on the beach with her friends, wearing a bathing suit, and her ED thoughts were fairly strong, telling her she was fatter than her friends, did not deserve to be wearing a bathing suit, and that she should not eat anything because she was already too fat. She took a deep breath and challenged those thoughts head on. She walked right up to the beach snack bar and ordered what she believed to be a very "unclean" or "unsafe" food, a basket of french fries. She held up the first fry, looked right at it, said some swearwords and proceeded to eat that fry slowly, trying to really taste each bite. She finished all of the fries in the basket and felt liberated. The voice in her head got quieter with each bite and with each successful challenge, and she was able to attend her desired college later that year.

So rest assured if you or someone you know is struggling with an eating disorder, you are not alone! We know the cure is not as simple as "Just eating." Trust your instincts, challenge yourself and your ED thoughts, and get help! Seeking treatment should not be seen as a failure or an embarrassment, but a means to recovery. You deserve recovery, and you can do it!

Written by Dr. Gabrielle (Lofaso) McAndrews, Psy.D., PC.

They say that having a child is like watching your heart walk around in somebody else's body. Well, in April of 2016 my heart was broken as I learned that my then 13-year-old daughter needed to be hospitalized for anorexia.

I distinctly remember being in the hospital room with my daughter as she refused to eat a single saltine cracker because it would make her fat. She was also in total denial that she was in the midst of an eating disorder. As she looked up at me with fear in her big brown eyes, I told her, "An eating disorder is like a force or monster that takes over your mind, your judgment, and your body, and right now, sweetie, you may feel helpless to fight up against it. But guess what, that eating disorder has to get through me to get to you!" Several minutes later, she ate that saltine cracker.

The irony is that I am a Clinical Psychologist myself. Over my thirty-five year career, I have treated many adults and adolescents, some of which had full blown eating disorders themselves. Yet when it came to my daughter, I needed to rely on the expertise of other professionals to help her. I felt utterly helpless. In addition to an amazing therapist and psychiatrist, we sought the treatment from Debra Spector, a Registered Dietitian who specializes in eating disorders. Debra was an integral and vital part of my daughter's treatment team and her recovery.

After one week of inpatient hospitalization, and two weeks of partial hospitalization, my daughter was in remission. We followed up with her therapist and Debra, and I am pleased to say that almost two years later, my daughter has not relapsed back into her eating disorder. She continues to deal with anxiety and depression; however, Debra taught my daughter all about how to make all foods fit, body image distortions, and how to cope with triggers around eating and weight.

As a parent of a child with an eating disorder, the fear and helplessness it engenders can feel completely overwhelming. It is a terrifying experience. However, having a treatment team, such as a good psychiatrist, therapist and registered dietitian, like Debra, allows you to feel hope and guidance. Debra was soft and empathetic, as well as strong and directive when it was necessary. Her years of training and experience were invaluable to my daughter's healing. We will forever be grateful to Debra for all she has done for my daughter, and our family; she was a beacon of hope during an otherwise hopeless and desperate time.

From her daughter, my patient : Thank you so much for your help, care, and dedication this year. We are blessed to know you and have your expertise.

Written by Agnes Wohl LCSW ACSW

Diplomat in Clinical Social Work
Member of National Center for Crisis Management

As a trauma therapist, my patients come in with their narrative all relating to the horrific life events that they have survived. Their complaints are hypervigilance, flashbacks, labile emotions, conflicts with family members, sexual issues, high anxiety as well as a host of other symptoms. As their stories and lives slowly reveal themselves, very often, eating disorders emerge that they, themselves, have not defined as one of their symptoms or in their own presentation, as a life interfering issue. They, like others, have used food (binging, purging, or the restriction of food) as a friend, a coping mechanism, or a way to tamp down the high level of emotions and/or to anesthetize themselves.

The eating disorder is low on their priority list of issues they want to change. It becomes my work, as their therapist, to balance dealing with the trauma, giving them new coping strategies and convincing them that the eating disorder is, in fact, life interfering. This is different from the patient who comes in presenting with an eating disorder and knows they need help with this issue. Therefore, in my work with the eating disorder it is more recalcitrant than other symptoms, as the patient is not asking for help in that area necessarily. This is due to the fact that it is effective, of course, in a destructive way, in managing all of the post-traumatic stress disorder symptoms. My job in addressing the eating disorder becomes more complex. First, I have to show the patient that this is, in fact, an issue and then to help them replace the eating disorder with healthy ways to manage their symptoms as well as very dysregulated emotions. Word to the wise: If you don't ask, it likely will not be presented. In addition, this usually involves a team approach including an internist, registered dietitian, and a psychiatrist.

From Emma R.

She had always had a birthday cake, but due to her anorexia, never gave herself permission to eat it:

So happy to say that this year I ate my birthday cake! I'm continuing to take challenges as part of my goal setting (eating with someone an unsafe food). She sent me many pictures of her and her friends at school breaking away from unsafe foods.

This picture was sent to me from Emma R. on 3/17

From Janine F.
*A patient I treated who is fully recovered from anorexia
and also suffered from severe OCD and trauma
(who couldn't eat messy food or white food in front of
anyone or watch other people eat it):*

A patient I treated who is fully recovered from anorexia and also suffered from severe OCD and trauma (who couldn't eat messy food or white food in front of anyone or watch other people eat it): When you're eating chicken wings and your eating disorder and OCD don't get in the way.

This picture was sent to me From Janine F. 2/17:

From Kristina A.
*A patient I treated who struggled with orthorexia (clean eating/fitness/
bodybuilding). We ate "unclean/processed" food together a few times.*

"I had a bite of a cannoli AND a martini on my birthday!"

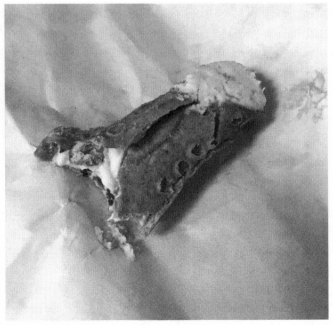

This picture was sent to me from Kristina A. on 6/17

ACKNOWLEDGEMENTS

Thank you for taking a chance on this book. The book became an indie project that brought the utmost respect to any author with an idea while not having a publisher or literary agent to help put their thoughts into publication.

To say this book has been on a journey in and of itself would be an understatement. The journey began in 2016 and has evolved, changed hands as well as direction more times than you can imagine!

I've said, "I quit, this is too hard and too much work" way too many times and would have loved to chuck it in the f**k- it bucket more times than imaginable!

My deepest gratitude goes first and foremost to the 23 people who contributed their personal testimonials in the hope that perhaps one of their essays will touch one of you readers and push you forward on the very difficult journey to recover from an eating disorder.

A special thanks to my son Jake for spending hours editing the editor with me and catching things that I never saw. Everyone should hire you! As always, I love you to the moon and back.

A heartfelt thank-you to my family; especially my sister Randi and my daughter Hannah, along with my close friends for reading, rereading, cheering me on, and spending endless time listening to me talk about the book over and over again and for your patience and understanding. I will be forever grateful.

This book would never have made it to the final stage of publication without my friend, graphic designer and illustrator and now fellow writer, Gary Macknight. Your expertise, knowledge, patience, and late nights will never be forgotten.

My editor Adele Brinkley, who was introduced to me by Tracy Stopler- a fellow RDN who also wrote two books in her not so spare time. Thank you Adele. My use of ellipses... CAPITALS along with "parenthesis" thank you as well.

I want to thank my colleagues and patients who have stuck by my side all of these years with my sass, direct use of potty words, and no sugar coating approach to motivate and guide those of you on a very difficult journey toward the other side of the wobbly bridge I've called recovery. You are the reason I have successfully upheld a private practice since 1990 doing a difficult job that I truly love.

Lastly, I want to thank my mom. My biggest fan. Since I was young, she would push me, share my work and ideas with anyone and everyone willing to listen. You are my first best friend. I love you more...

Personally, as an avid reader myself in two book clubs, I often read the acknowledgment page first to get a feel for the author of the book I may choose to read. You may have done the same. With that said, of course acknowledging the above is extremely important, but not as important as thanking YOU, the reader of this book. You somehow came across it in your search to try and "figure it out", see if anyone could understand what you're going through. I truly hope you have found this book of relational essays helpful in guiding you to your next step on your journey to recovery.

I know, your struggle is real...

Debra Spector, MS, RDN, CDN

Made in the USA
Middletown, DE
10 October 2021